Daily TEKS Review

WORKBOOK

PEARSON

Glenview, Illinois • Boston, Massachusetts • Chandler, Arizona • Upper Saddle River, New Jersey

PEARSON

ISBN-13: 978-0-328-78225-3
ISBN-10: 0-328-78225-4

6 7 8 9 10 V011 17 16 15

Contents

Name ______________________________

Daily TEKS Review
1-1

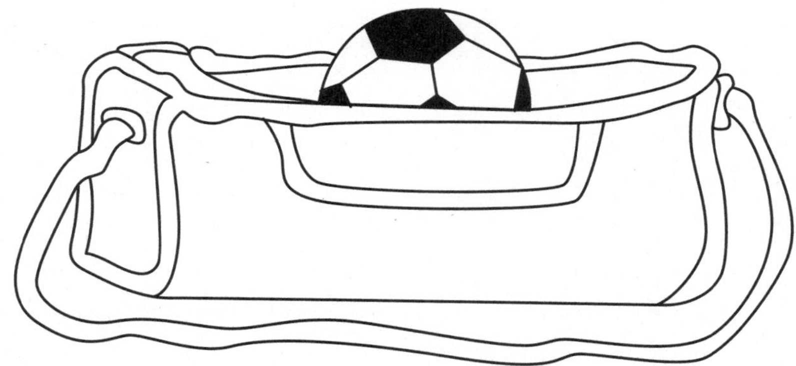

Directions Have students: 1 fill in the bubble next to the picture that shows 3 teddy bears; 2 color the boxes to show how many soccer balls are in the bag.

Name ______________________________

Daily TEKS Review
1-2

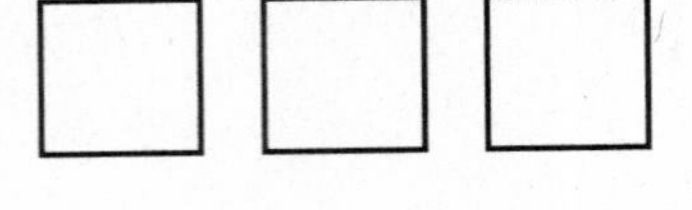

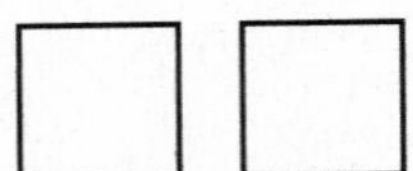

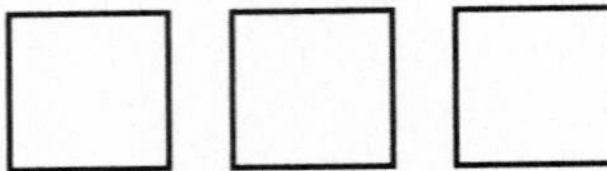

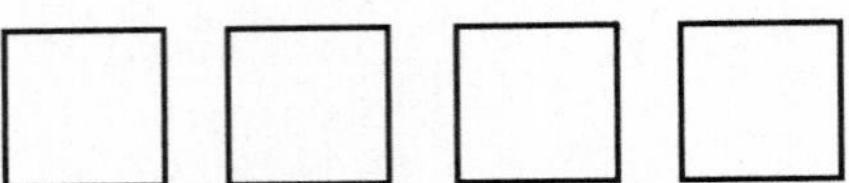

Directions Have students: 1 fill in the bubble next to the picture that shows 2 stars; 2 circle the picture with the same number of boxes as the top.

Name ___________________________________

Daily TEKS Review
1-3

- ○ 1
- ○ 2
- ○ 3
- ○ 4

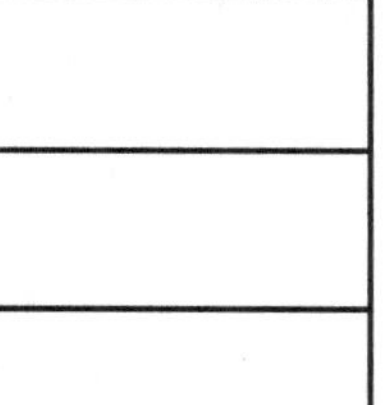

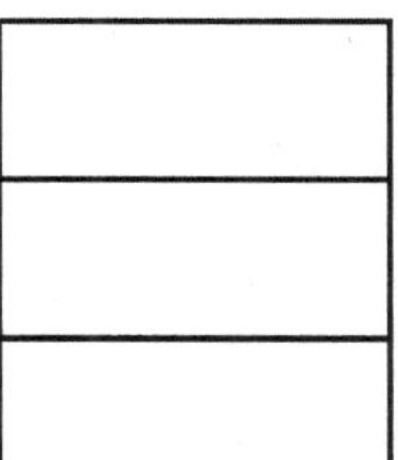

Directions Have students: 1 fill in the bubble next to the number that tells how many animals; 2–3 count the animals, and then color the boxes to show how many.

Name ______________________

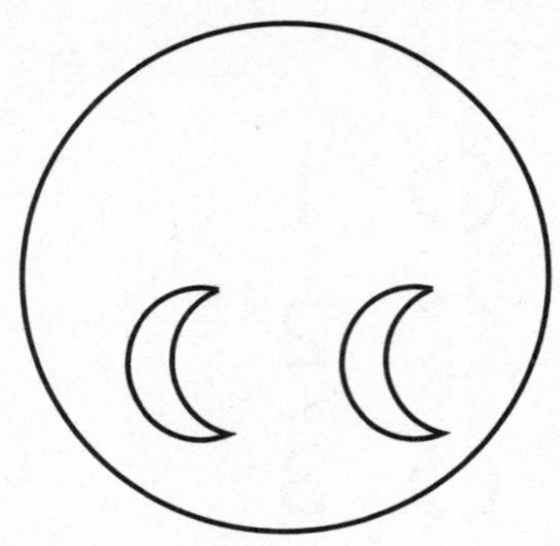

- ○ 4
- ○ 3
- ○ 2
- ○ 1

2

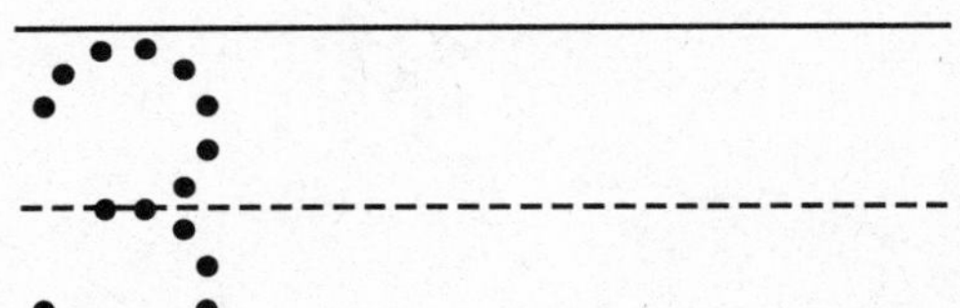

3

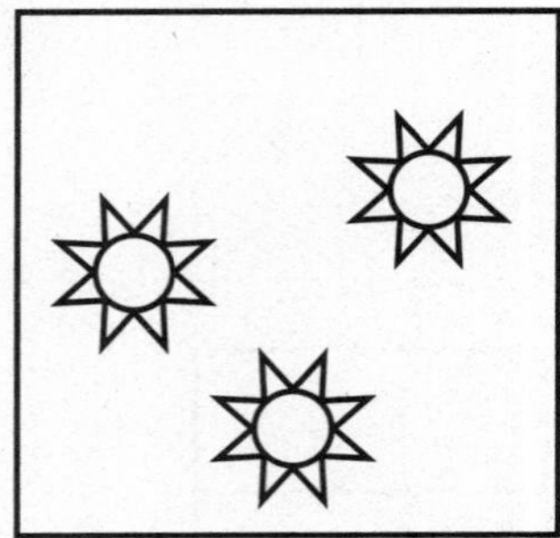

Directions Have students: 1 fill in the bubble next to the number that tells how many moons; 2 count the stars, and then practice writing the number that tells how many; 3 count the suns, and then draw the same number of counters in the box to show how many.

Name ______________________________

Daily TEKS Review 1-5

1

○ 2

○ 3

○ 4

○ 5

2

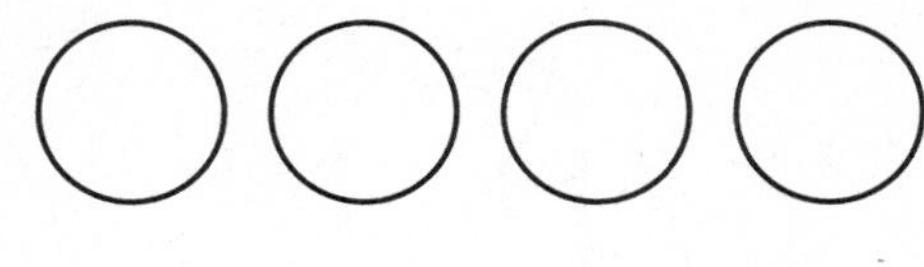

○ ◯

○ ◯ ◯

○ ◯ ◯ ◯

○ ◯ ◯ ◯ ◯

3

Directions Have students: 1 fill in the bubble next to the number that tells how many horses; 2 fill in the bubble next to the picture that shows the same number of counters as the top; 3 count the leaves on the tree, and then write the number that tells how many.

Name ______________________________

○ 2

○ 3

○ 4

○ 5

2

Directions Have students: 1 fill in the bubble next to the number that tells how many boats; 2 circle the group that has 5 counters.

Name ___

○ 

○ 

○ 

○ 

2

1	2	3	4
○	○	○	○

3

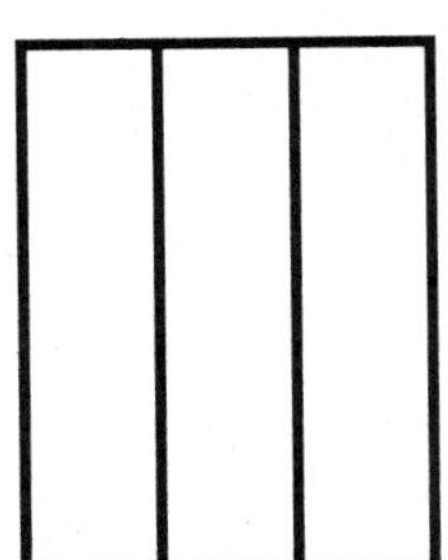

Directions Have students: 1 fill in the bubble next to the picture with 1 fork; 2 fill in the bubble below the number that tells how many books; 3 count the ducks, and then color the boxes to show how many.

Name ________________________________

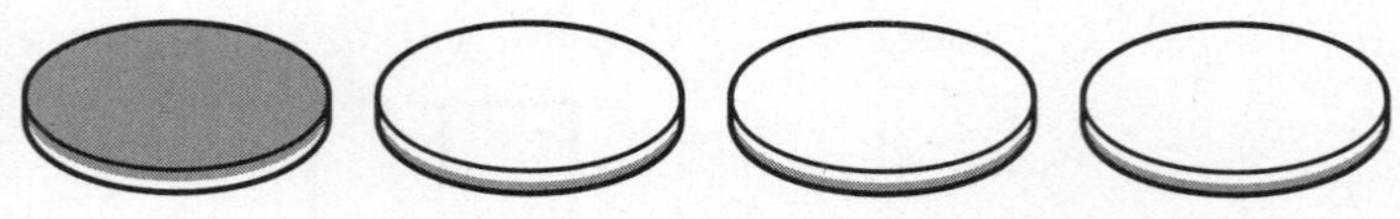

Directions Have students: 1 fill in the bubble next to the picture with 4 forks; 2 fill in the bubble next to the number that tells how many books; 3 look at this way to make 4, and then color the counters in the bottom row to show a different way to make 4.

Name ______________________________

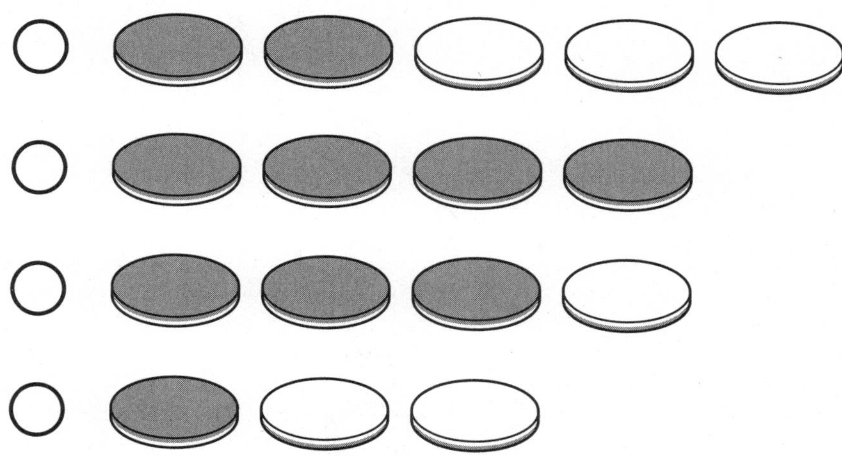

2

Directions Have students: **1** fill in the bubble next to the picture that shows a way to make 5; **2** count the birds, and then color the boxes to show how many.

Name ___________________________________

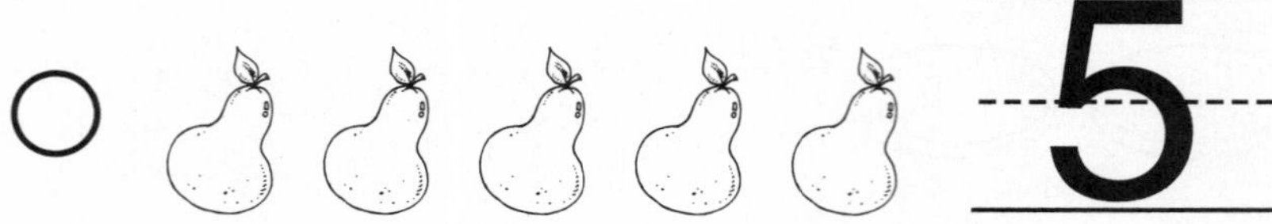

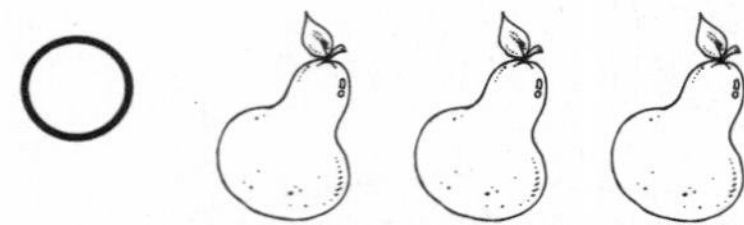

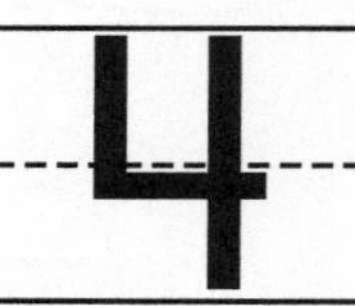

3

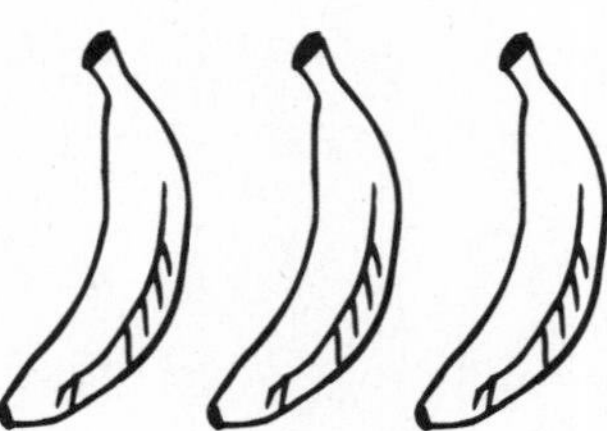

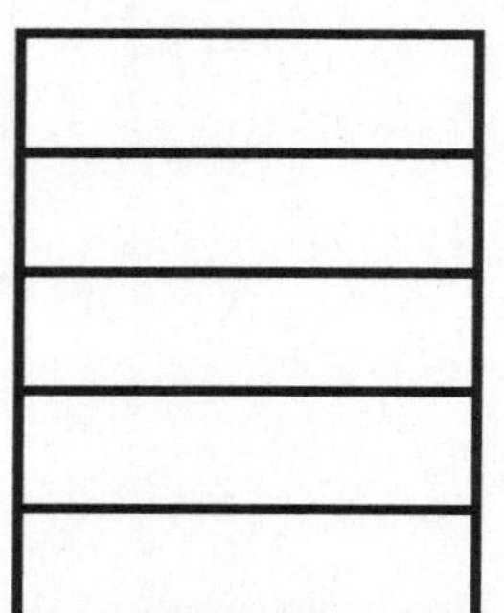

Directions Have students: 1 fill in the bubble next to the picture that shows 2 apples; 2 fill in the bubble next to the picture that shows the number 4; 3 count the bananas, and then color the boxes to show how many.

Name ______________________________

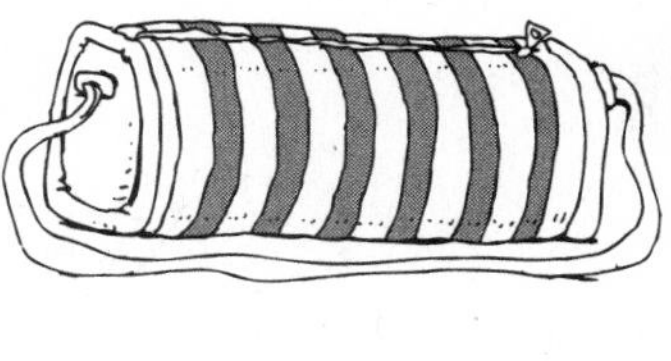

5 ○ 4 ○ 3 ○ 2 ○

Directions Have students: 1 count the soccer balls in each bag, and then write the numbers that tell how many; 2 fill in the bubble next to the picture that shows 2 stars; 3 fill in the bubble below the number that tells how many hearts.

Name ________________

2

○ 1

○ 2

○ 3

○ 4

Directions Have students: 1 circle the group of animals that has more than the others; 2 fill in the bubble next to the number that tells how many ducks.

Name ______________________

○ 4

○ 3

○ 2

○ 1

2

Directions Have students: 1 fill in the bubble next to the number that tells how many shells; 2 draw counters to show the same number of counters as water bottles.

Name ________________________________

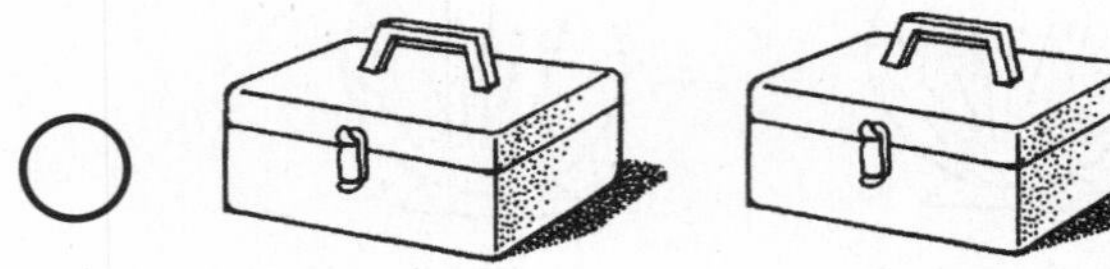 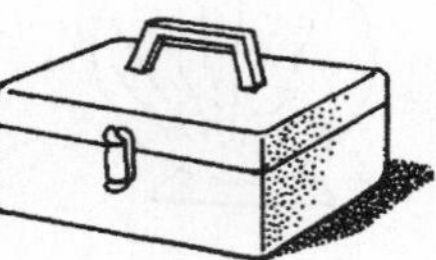 

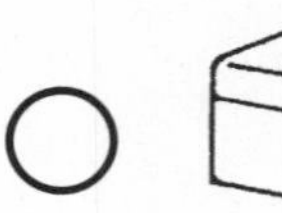 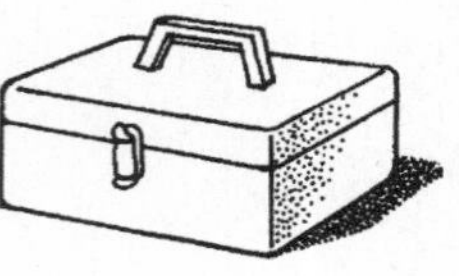  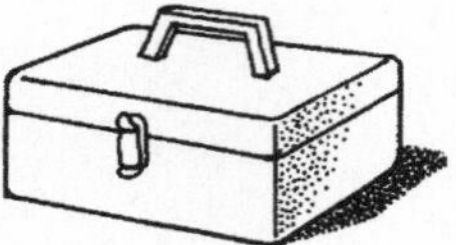

 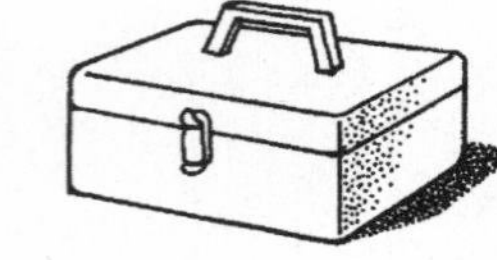 

Directions Have students: 1 fill in the bubble next to the picture that shows 3 cases; 2 draw counters to show 2 fewer counters than bears.

Name ______________________________

○ 5

○ 4

○ 3

○ 2

2

Directions Have students: 1 fill in the bubble next to the number that tells how many frogs; 2 draw counters to show 2 more counters than birds.

Name ______________________________

1

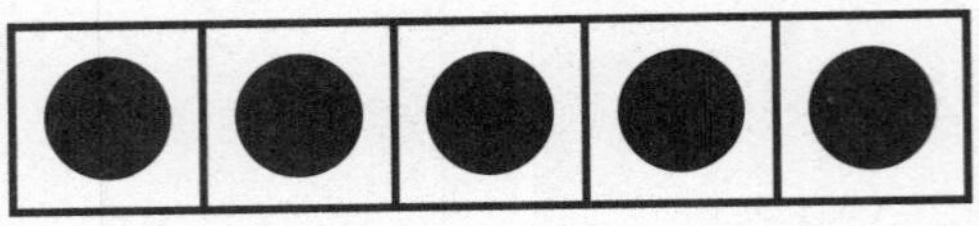

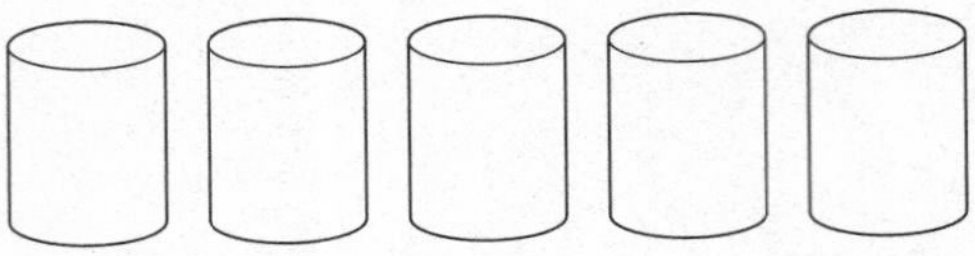

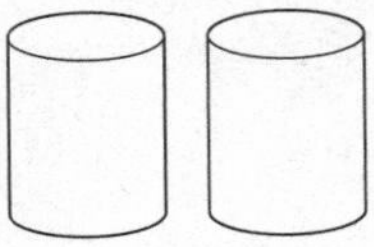

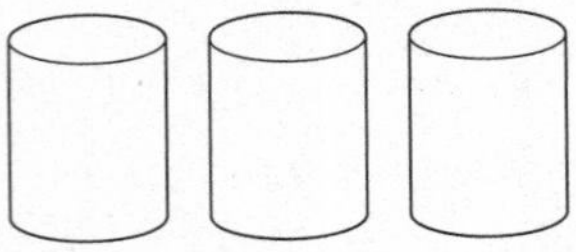

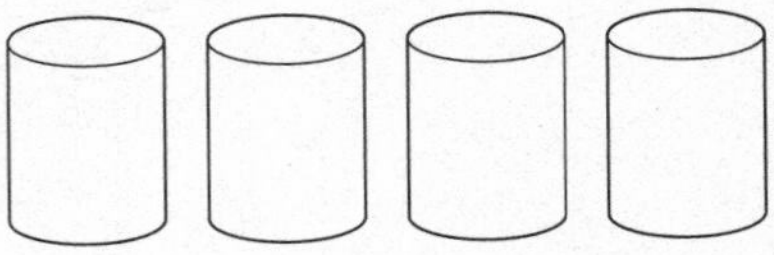

2

3

Directions Have students: 1 fill in the bubble next to the picture that shows the same number of blocks as counters; 2 fill in the bubble next to the picture that shows 5 horses; 3 draw a group with 1 fewer bug than the group shown, and then write the number that tells how many.

Name ______________________________

Daily TEKS Review
3-2

1

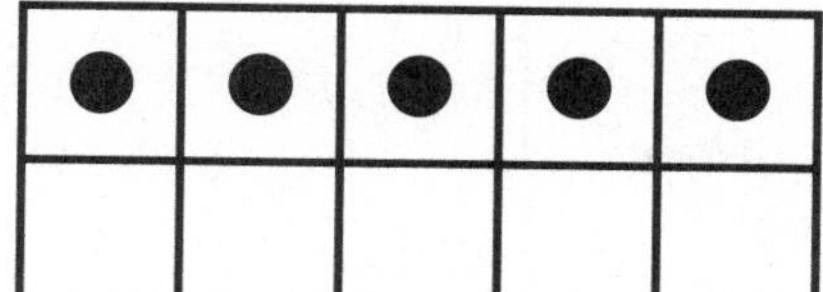

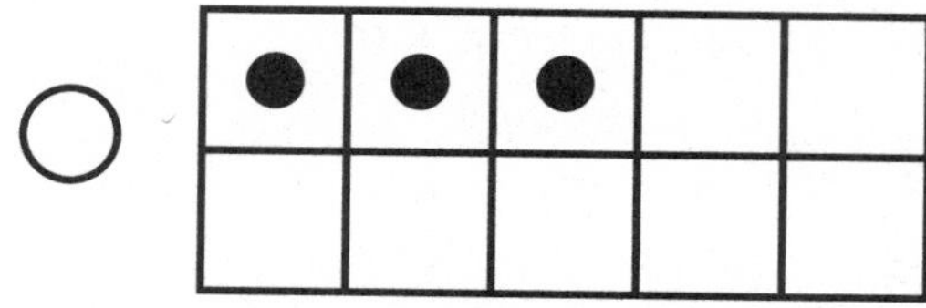

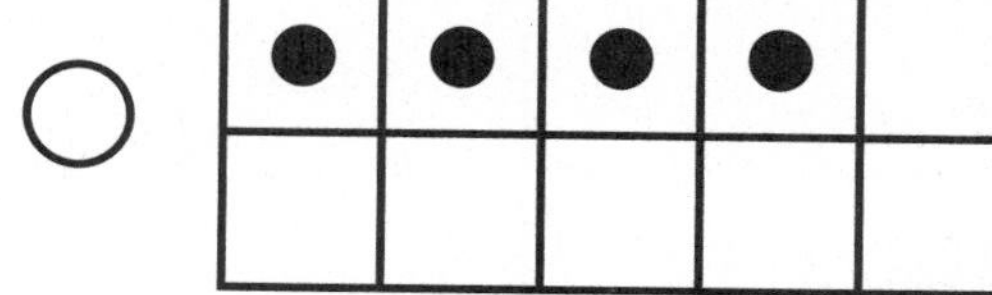

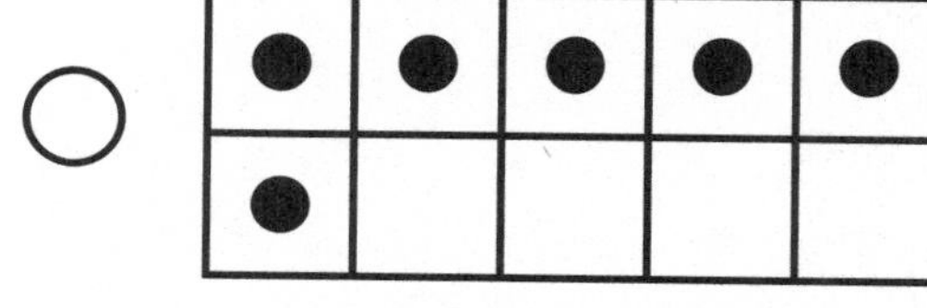

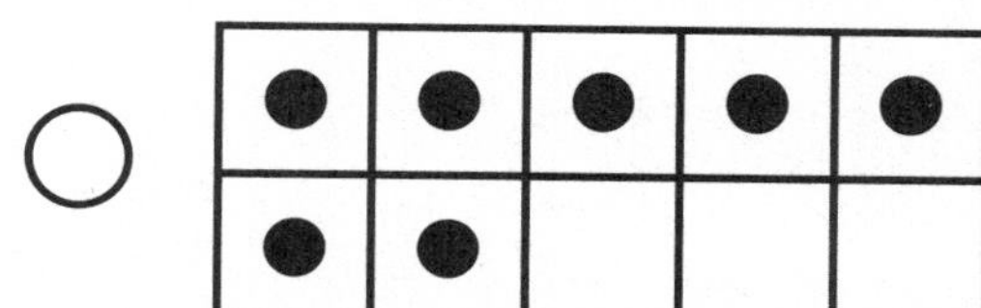

2

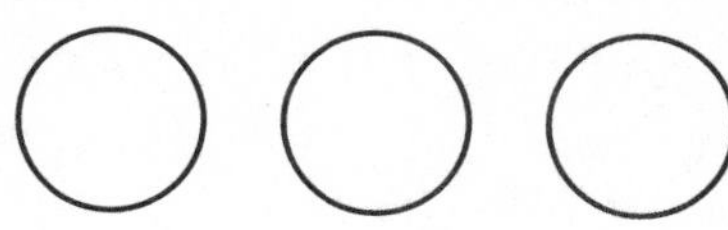

○ 2

○ 3

○ 4

○ 5

3

Directions Have students: 1 fill in the bubble next to the ten-frame that shows 2 more counters than the ten-frame at the top; 2 fill in the bubble next to the number that tells how many counters; 3 draw a group that has 2 fewer books than the group shown.

Name ________________________________

Daily TEKS Review
3-3

0 ○ | ○ 2 ○ 3 ○

2

○ 

○ 

○ 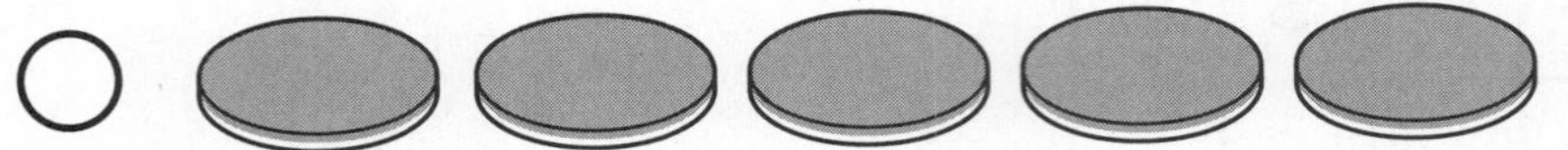

○ 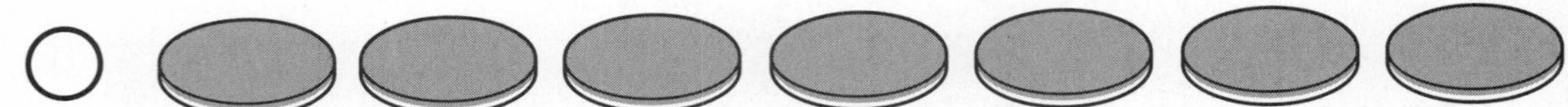

3

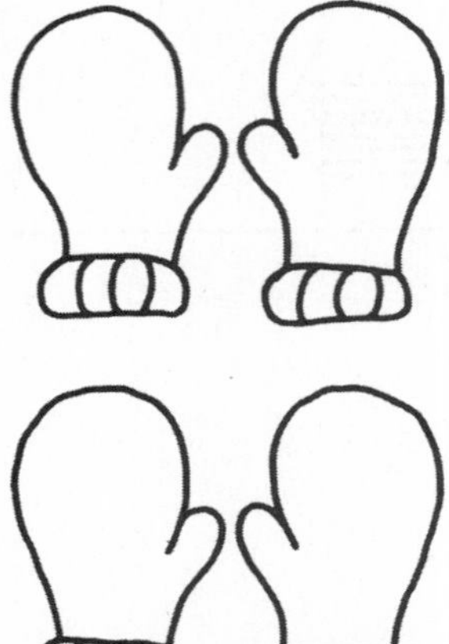

Directions Have students: 1 fill in the bubble next to the number that tells how many books; 2 fill in the bubble next to the picture that shows 6 counters; 3 draw a group that has 1 fewer mitten than the group shown.

Name ______________________________

Daily TEKS Review
3-4

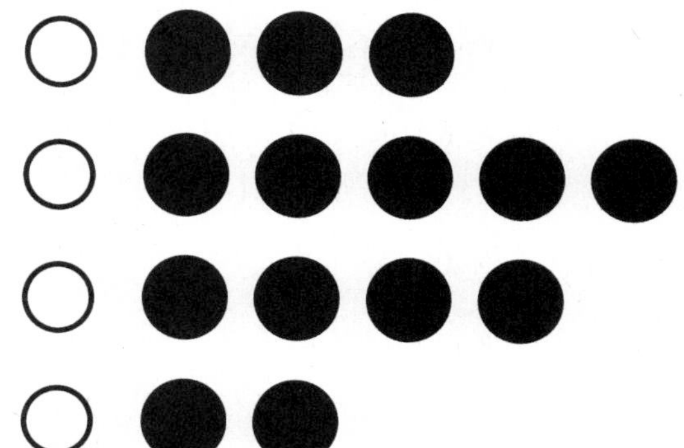

______________ ______________

Directions Have students: 1 fill in the bubble next to the picture that shows 7 geese; 2 fill in the bubble next to the picture that shows 4 counters; 3 count the number of water bottles, and then write the number that tells how many two times.

Name ___________________

○ 0 ○ 2

○ 1 ○ 3

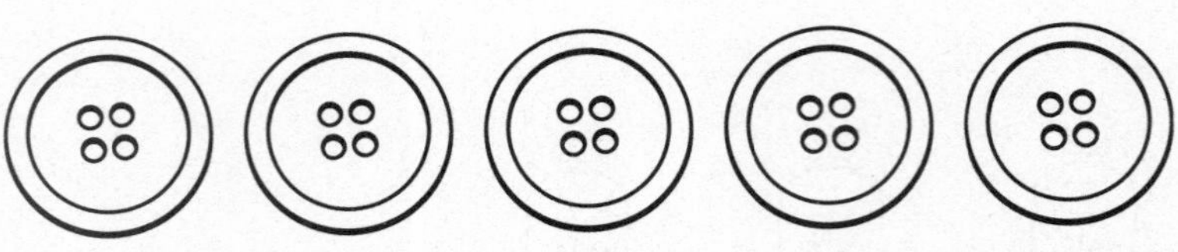

Directions Have students: 1 fill in the bubble next to the picture that shows 8 swans; 2 fill in the bubble next to the number that tells how many crayons there are in the box; 3 draw a group that has 2 more buttons than the group shown.

Name ______________________

1

○ 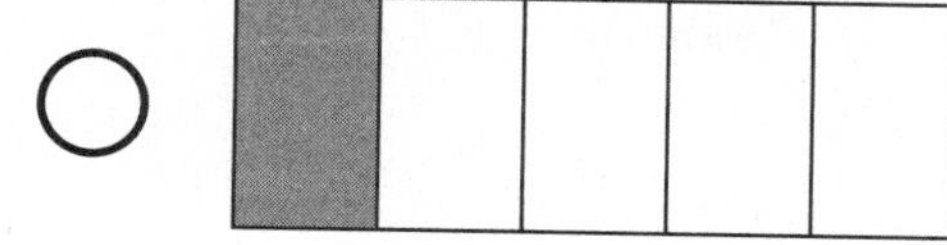

○ 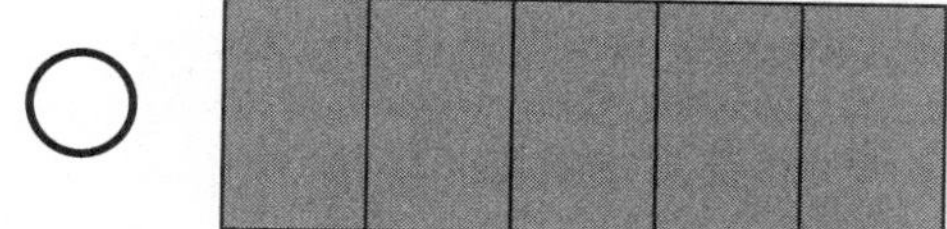

○ 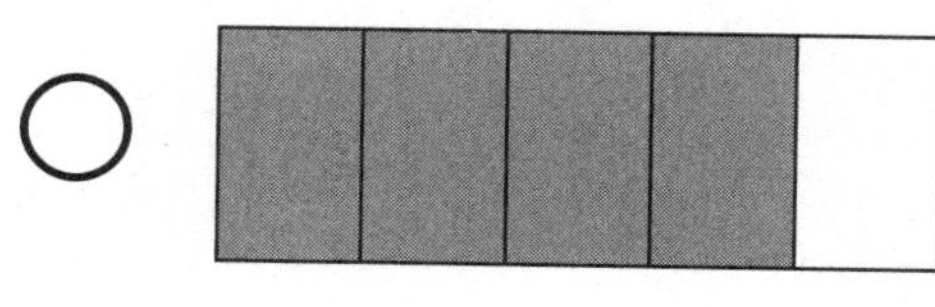

○ 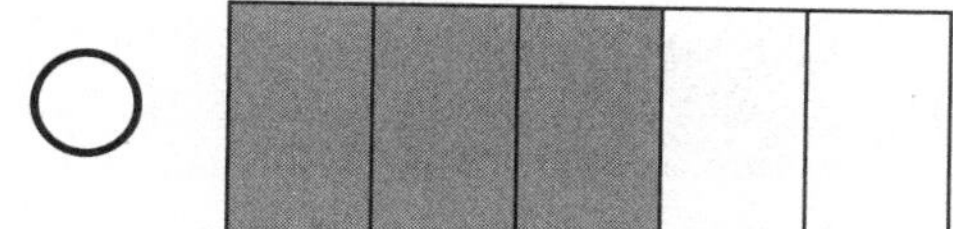

2

○ 0

○ 1

○ 2

○ 3

3

Directions Have students: 1 fill in the bubble next to the picture that shows 5 shaded boxes; 2 fill in the bubble next to the number that tells how many babies are in the baby buggy; 3 draw counters to show 9.

Name ______________________

1

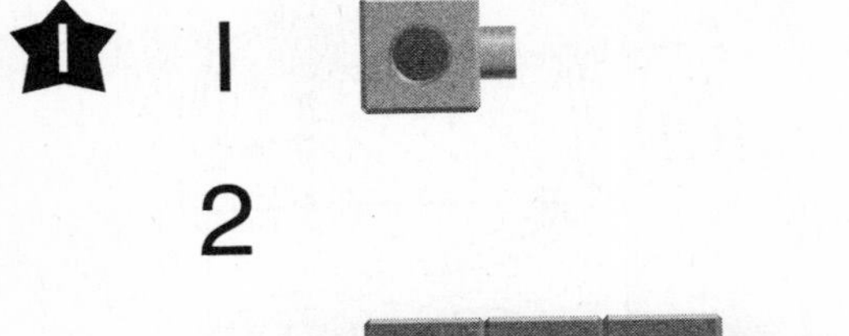

2

2

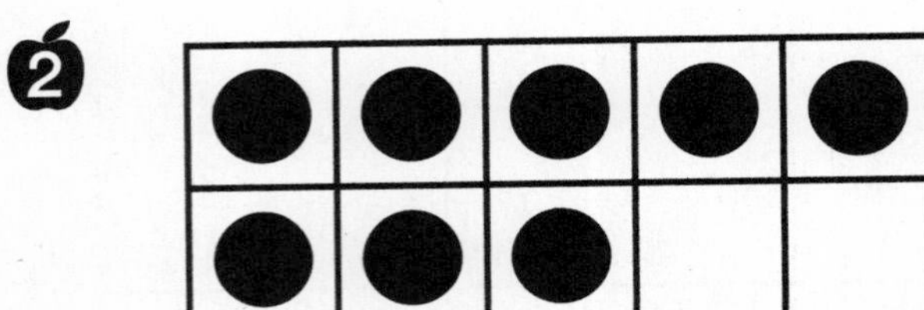

6 ○ 7 ○ 8 ○ 9 ○

3

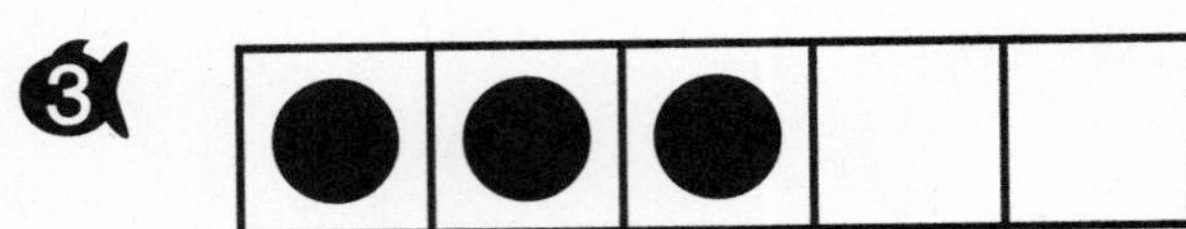

Directions Have students: 1 fill in the bubble next to the picture that shows the missing number of cubes when counting in order from 1 to 5; 2 fill in the bubble below the number that tells how many counters; 3 draw counters in the five-frame to show 2 more.

Name ___________________________

1

○ 7 ○ 8 ○ 9 ○ 10

2

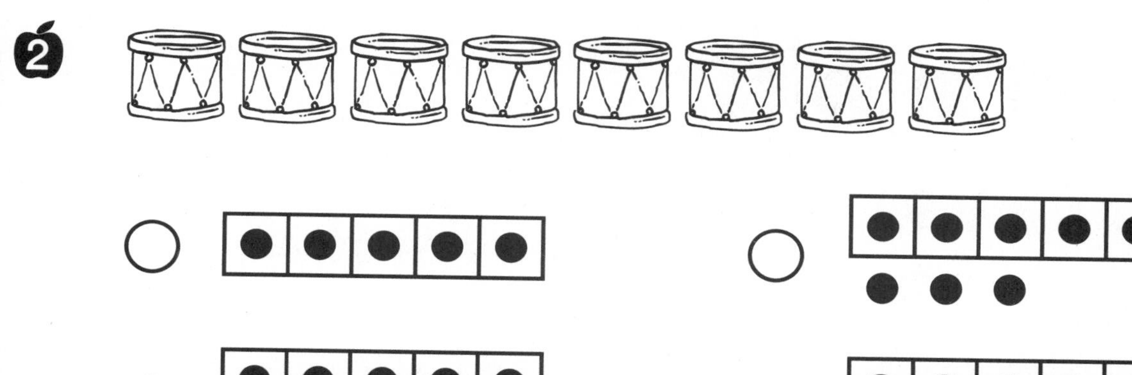

3

Directions Have students: 1 fill in the bubble next to the number that tells how many children; 2 fill in the bubble next to the picture that shows how many drums; 3 count the pieces of fruit, and then color the boxes to show how many.

Name ______________________________

1

2

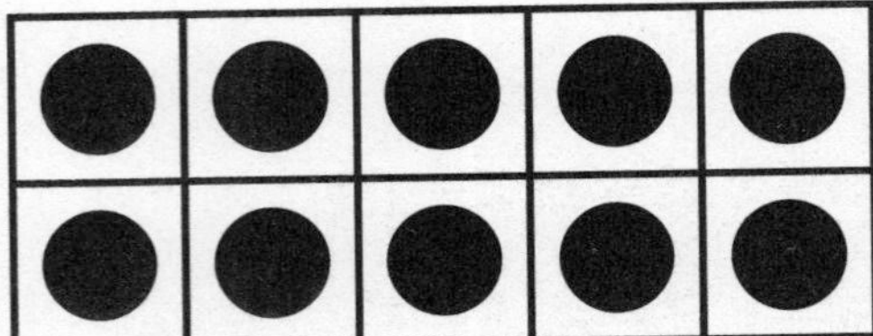

10 9 1 0

3

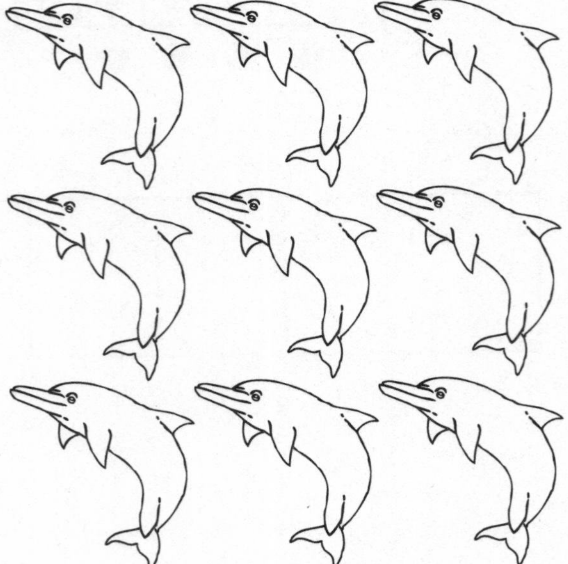

Directions Have students: 1 fill in the bubble next to the picture that shows 7 counters; 2 fill in the bubble below the number that tells how many counters; 3 count the dolphins, and then write the number that tells how many three times.

Name ______________________

Daily TEKS Review
3-10

1

4 ○ 8 ○ 9 ○ 10 ○

2

______

______

Directions Have students: 1 fill in the bubble below the number that tells how many cats; 2 draw a picture that shows ten counters or objects, and then write the number that tells how many.

Name ____________________

Daily TEKS Review
4-1

1

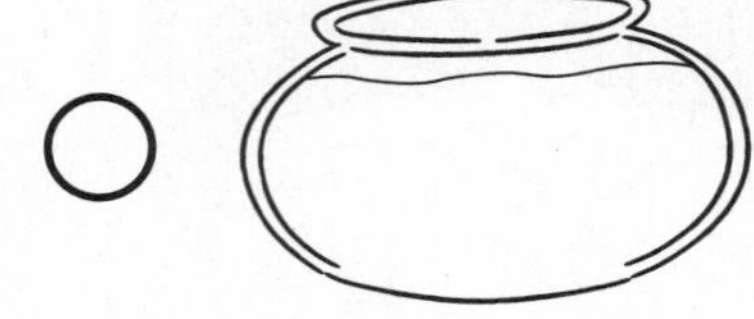

3

Directions Have students: 1 fill in the bubble next to the picture that shows the fishbowl with 0 fish; 2 fill in the bubble next to the picture that shows 2 birds on the branch; 3 count the stars, and then write the number that tells how many two times.

Name ______________________________

1

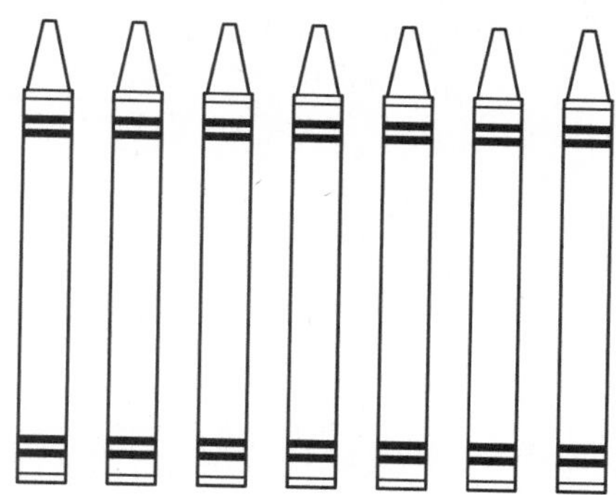

○ 5

○ 6

○ 7

○ 8

2 4

○ △

○ △ △

○ △ △ △

○ △ △ △ △

3

Directions Have students: 1 fill in the bubble next to the number that tells how many crayons; 2 fill in the bubble next to the picture that shows 4 shapes; 3 draw a group that has 1 fewer button than the group shown.

Name ______________________

Daily TEKS Review
4-3

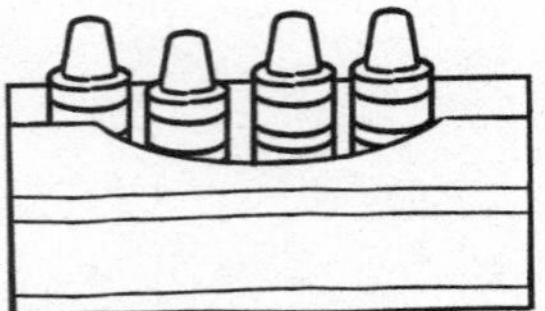

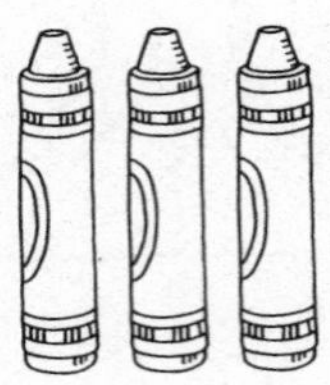

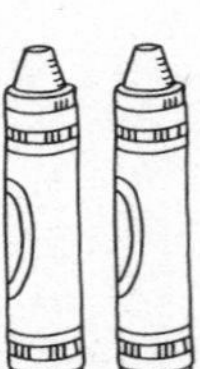

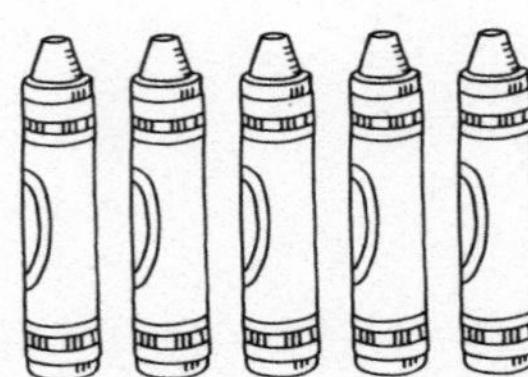

Directions Have students: 1 fill in the bubble next to the picture that shows a group of 6 hearts; 2 circle the picture that shows a number of crayons that is greater than the number of crayons in the box.

Name ______________________

Daily TEKS Review
4-4

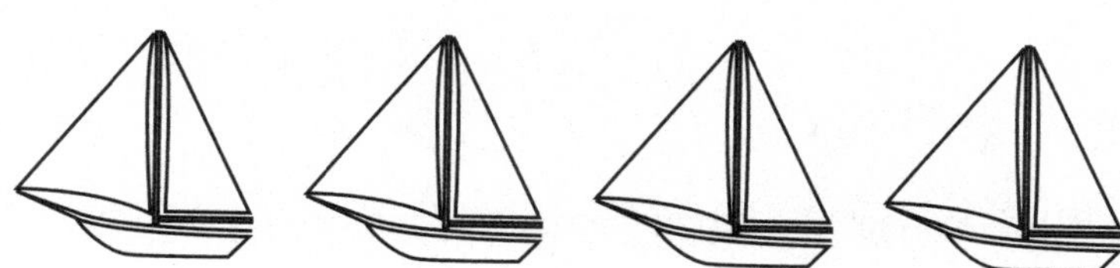

○ 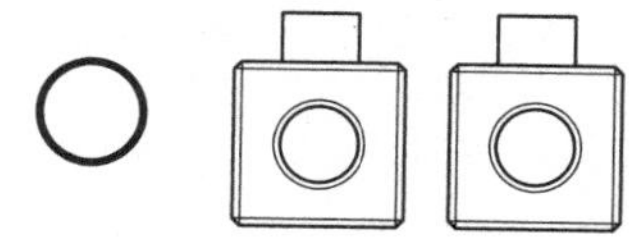

○ 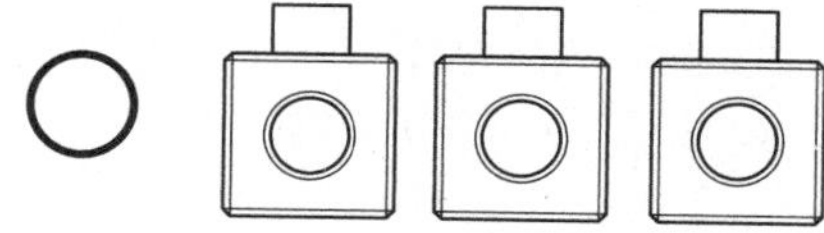

○ 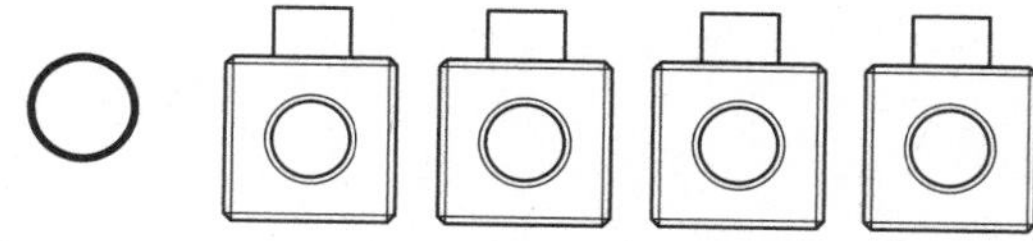

○ 

2

______

Directions Have students: 1 fill in the bubble next to the picture that shows the same number of cubes as boats; 2 count the number of fish in the tank, and then write the number that tells how many.

Name ____________________

○ 7

○ 8

○ 9

○ 10

2

Directions Have students: 1 fill in the bubble next to the number that tells how many stickers; 2 circle the group that shows fewer stars than the group in the box.

Name ______________________

Daily TEKS Review
4-6

○ 

○ 

○ 

○ 

2 5, 6, 7, __?__

○ 8

○ 6

○ 5

○ 4

3 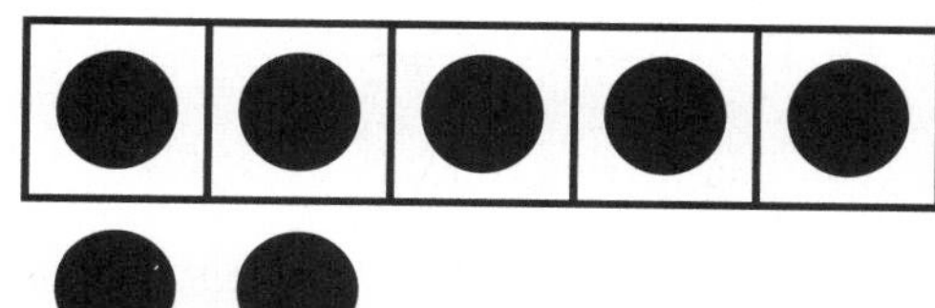

______

______

Directions Have students: 1 fill in the bubble next to the picture that shows a group of 3 hearts; 2 fill in the bubble next to the number that comes next; 3 draw more counters to make ten, and then write the number that tells how many.

Name ______________________

Daily TEKS Review
5-1

- ◯ 11
- ◯ 10
- ◯ 9
- ◯ 8

2

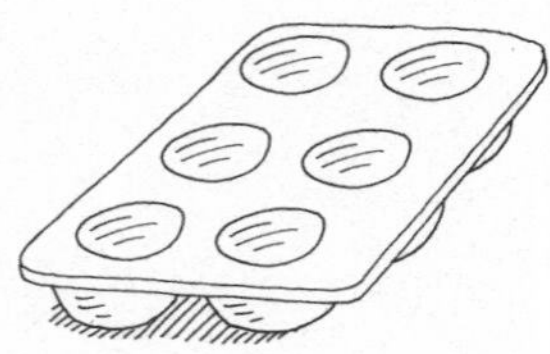

0	1	5	10
◯	◯	◯	◯

3

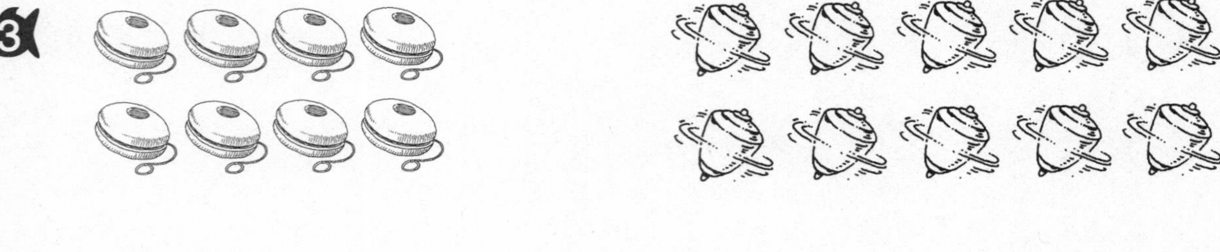

______________ ______________

Directions Have students: 1 fill in the bubble next to the number that tells how many spoons; 2 fill in the bubble below the number that tells how many muffins; 3 count the toys in each group, and then write the numbers that tell how many.

Name ____________________

Daily TEKS Review
5-2

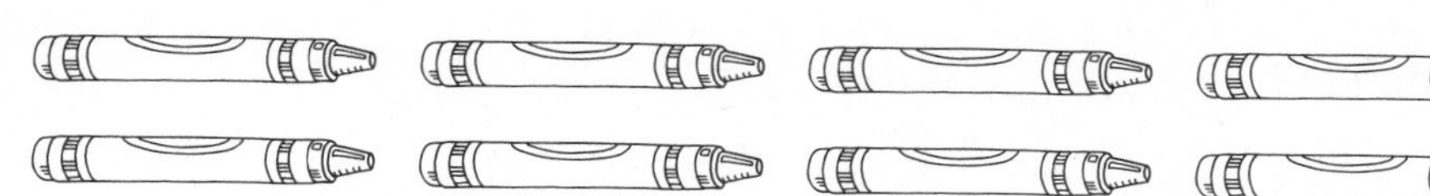
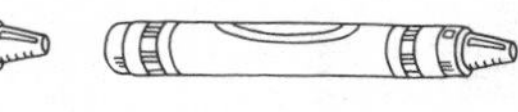

11 ○ 12 ○ 13 ○ 15 ○

2

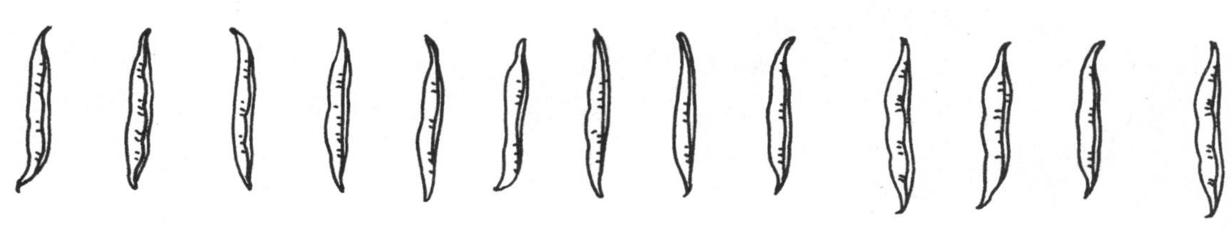

○ 9

○ 13

○ 14

○ 15

3

Directions Have students: 1 fill in the bubble below the number that tells how many crayons; 2 fill in the bubble next to the number that tells how many string beans; 3 draw Jerry's 11 bouncy balls.

Name ______________________________

1 15

14 15 16 17

○ ○ ○ ○

2

○ 11

○ 12

○ 13

○ 14

3

______

Directions Have students: 1 fill in the bubble below the number that is less than 15; 2 fill in the bubble next to the number that tells how many ducks; 3 count the cubes, and then write the number that tells how many in all.

Name ______________________________

Daily TEKS Review
5-4

○ 17

○ 18

○ 19

○ 20

Directions Have students: 1 fill in the bubble next to the number that tells how many trees; 2 count the hats, and then write the number that tells how many.

Name ______________________

1

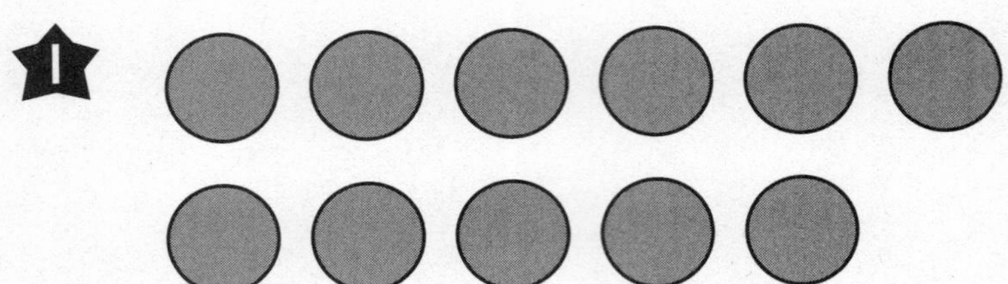

○ 14

○ 13

○ 12

○ 11

2

3	2	4	6	5
______	______	______	______	______

Directions Have students: 1 fill in the bubble next to the number that tells how many counters; 2 write the numbers in order.

Name ________________________________

1

○ 12

○ 13

○ 14

○ 15

2

○ 0 1 2 3 4 5

○ 5 4 0 1 3 2

○ 0 3 4 5 2 1

○ 5 4 0 1 2 3

3

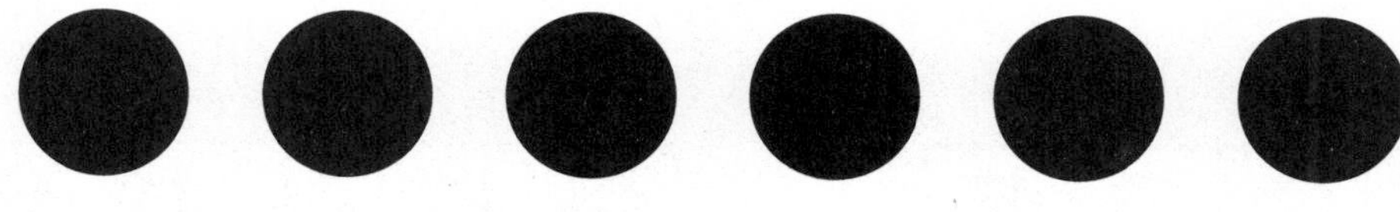

Directions Have students: 1 fill in the bubble next to the number that tells how many beach balls; 2 fill in the bubble next to the numbers that are in the correct order; 3 count the shapes, and then circle the group that has more.

Name ______________________________

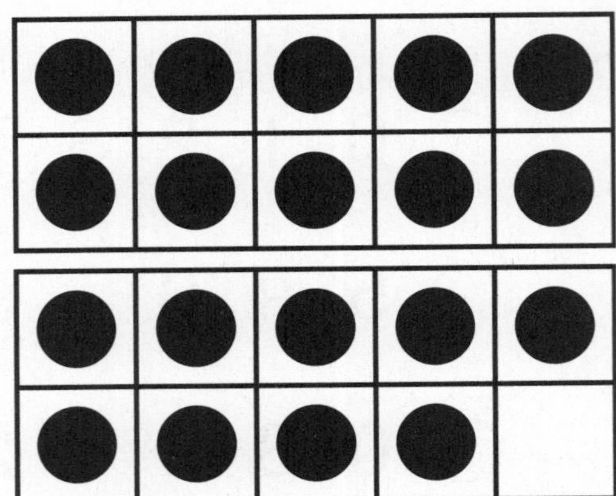

○ 16

○ 17

○ 18

○ 19

2

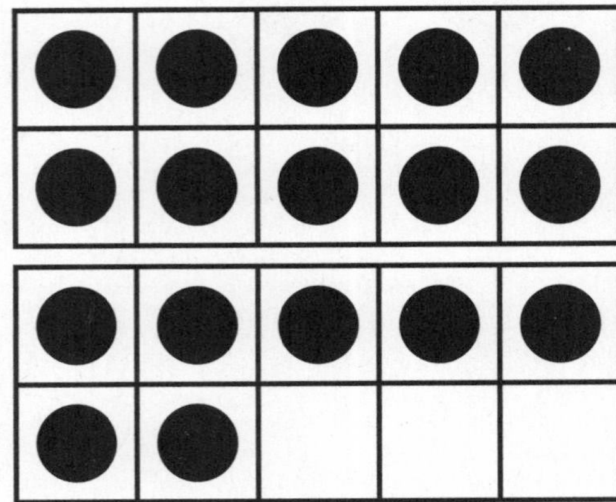

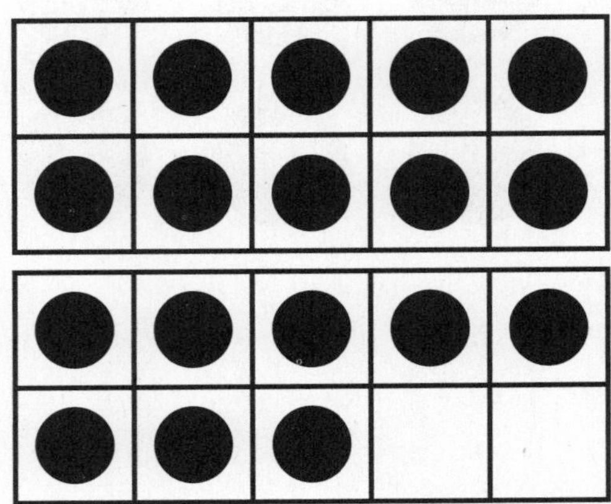

Directions Have students: 1 fill in the bubble next to the number that tells how many counters; 2 count the counters in each set, and then circle the set that has fewer.

Name ______________________________

Daily TEKS Review
5-8

○ 9

○ 10

○ 11

○ 12

2

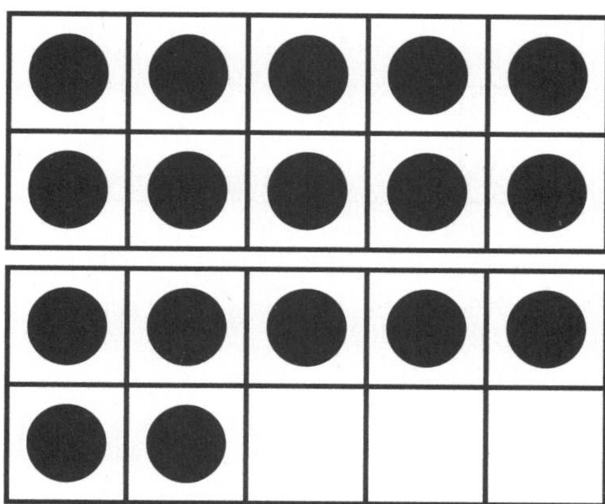

Directions Have students: 1 fill in the bubble next to the number that tells how many counters; 2 count the counters in each set, and then circle the set that has more.

Name ______________________________

1

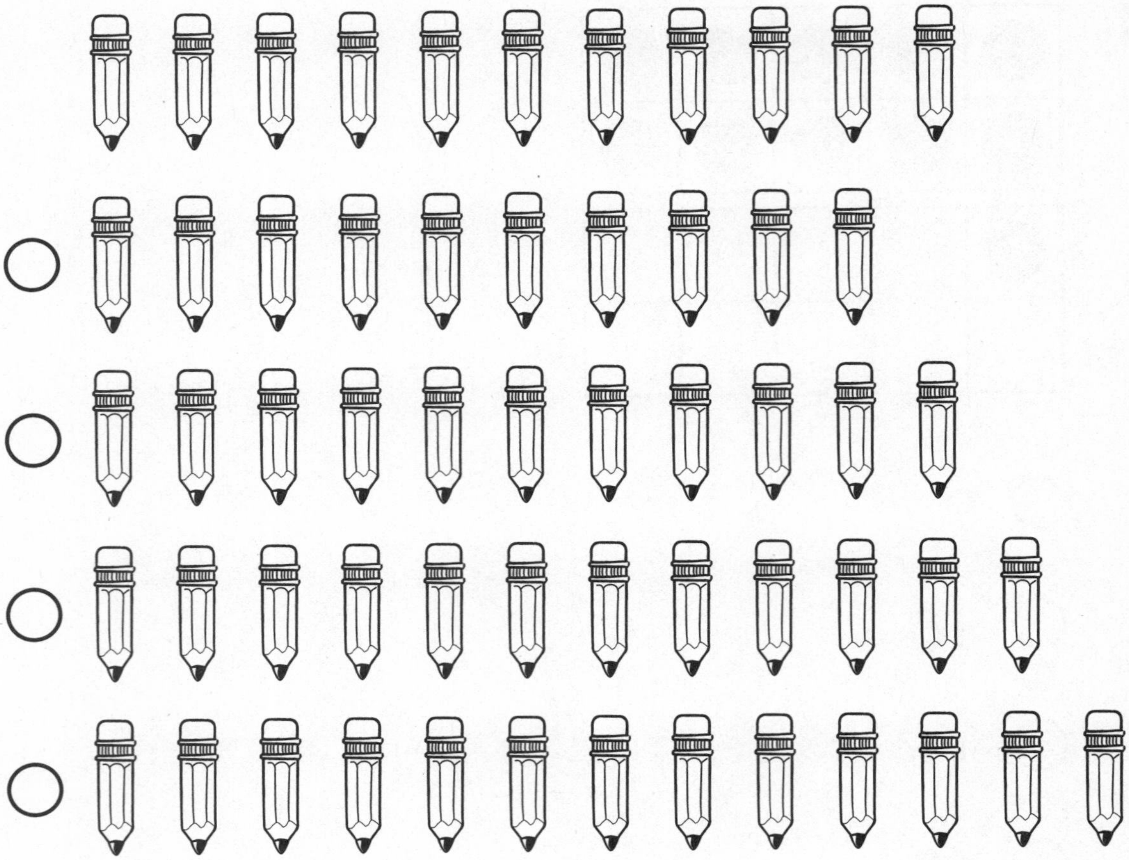

○

○

○

○

2

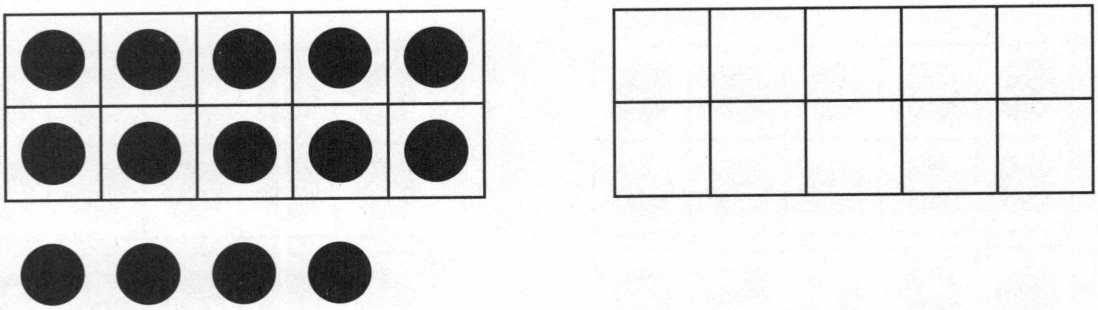

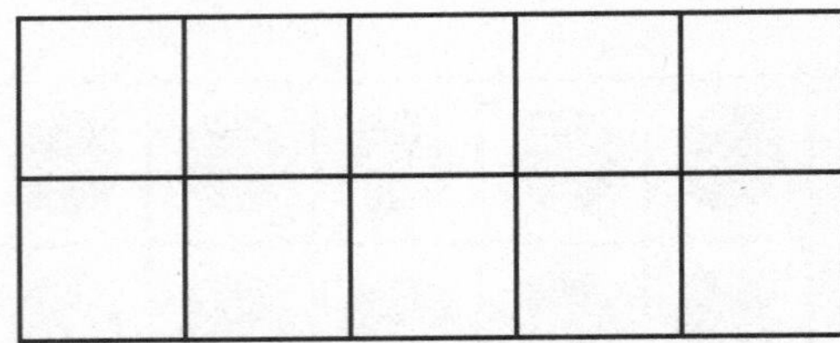

Directions Have students: 1 fill in the bubble next to the group that shows 1 more pencil than the group at the top; 2 draw a set with 1 fewer counter than the set shown.

Name ______________________________

Daily TEKS Review
5-10

2

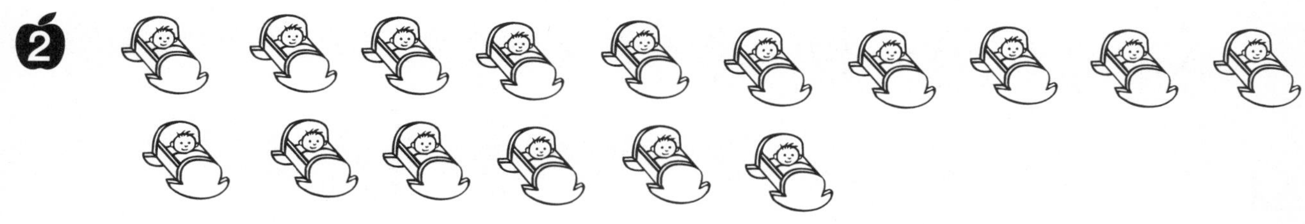

Directions Have students: 1 fill in the bubble next to the group that shows 2 more kittens than the group at the top; 2 count the babies, and then write the number that tells how many.

Name ____________________

Daily TEKS Review
6-1

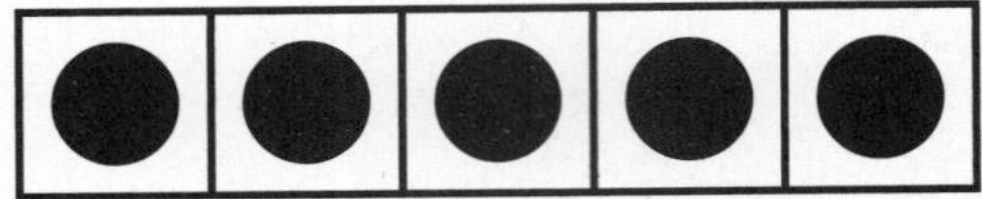

○ 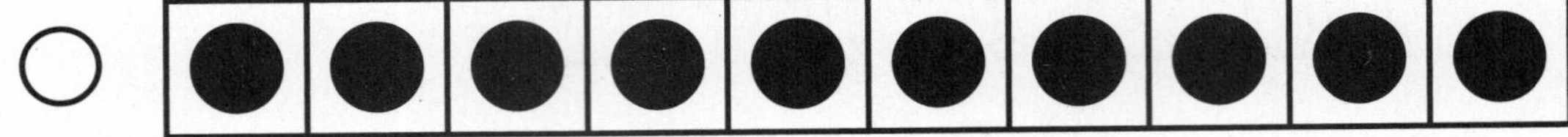

○ 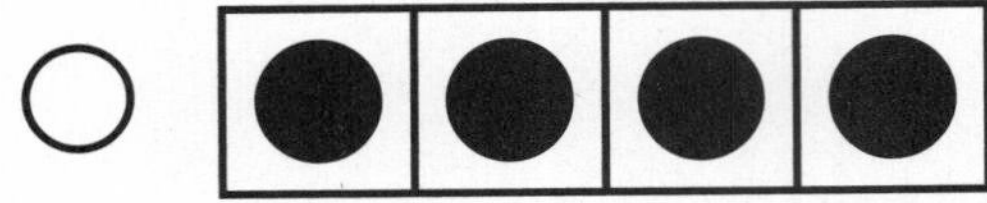

○ 

○ 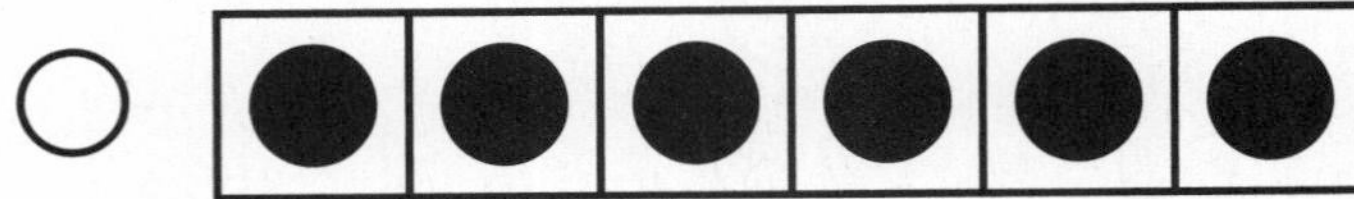

2 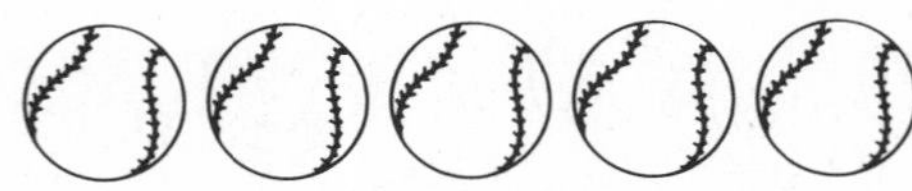

○ 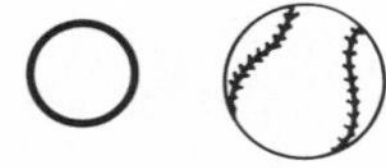

○ 

○ 

○ 

3

14

12

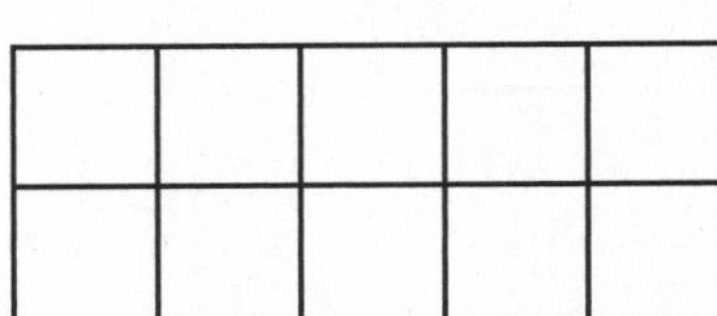

Directions Have students: 1 fill in the bubble next to the picture that shows a group of counters that has fewer than the group at the top; 2 fill in the bubble next to the picture that shows 1 fewer baseball than the group at the top; 3 draw counters in and below the ten-frames to show the numbers.

Name ______________________

1

2

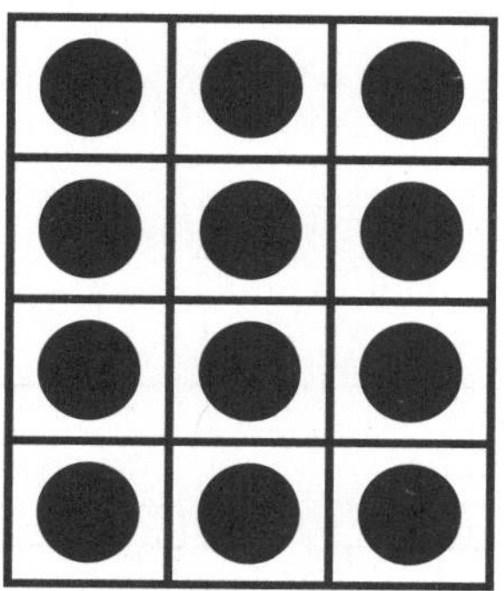

Directions Have students: 1 fill in the bubble next to the picture that shows 11 cherries; 2 count the counters in each set, and then write the numbers that tell how many.

Name ______________________

1

○ 13
○ 14
○ 15
○ 16

2

○ 12
○ 13
○ 14
○ 15

3

8	7	10	6	9

Directions Have students: 1 fill in the bubble next to the number that tells how many daisies; 2 fill in the bubble next to the number that tells how many trees; 3 write the numbers from the number cards in order from 6 to 10.

Name ______________________________

1 15

16 ○   17 ○   18 ○   19 ○

2 17

○ 

○ 

○ 

○ 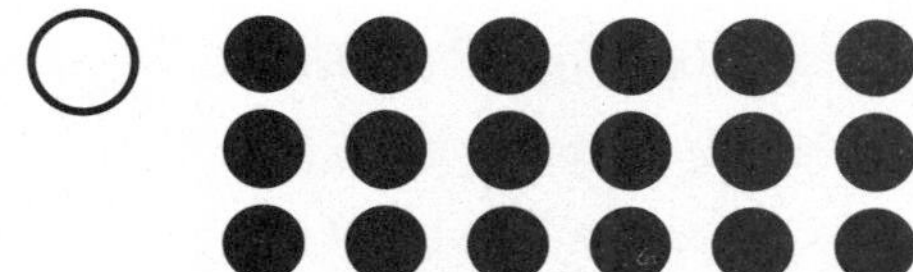

3 

____

Directions Have students: **1** fill in the bubble next to the number that is 2 more than 15; **2** fill in the bubble next to the set that has more than 17; **3** count the monkeys, and then write the number that tells how many.

Name ________________________________

1 2

○  ○ 

○  ○ 

2

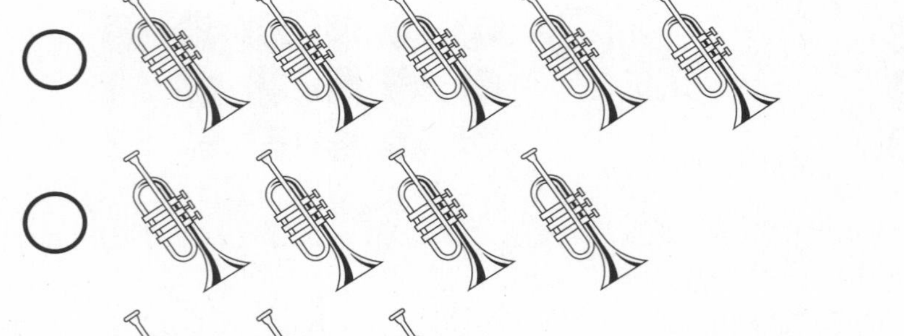

○

○

○

○ 

3

28

______

Directions Have students: 1 fill in the bubble next to the picture that shows 1 fewer than 2; 2 fill in the bubble next to the group that shows the same number of trumpets as the group at the top; 3 write the number for 1 more than 28.

Name ______________________________

○ 

○ 

○ 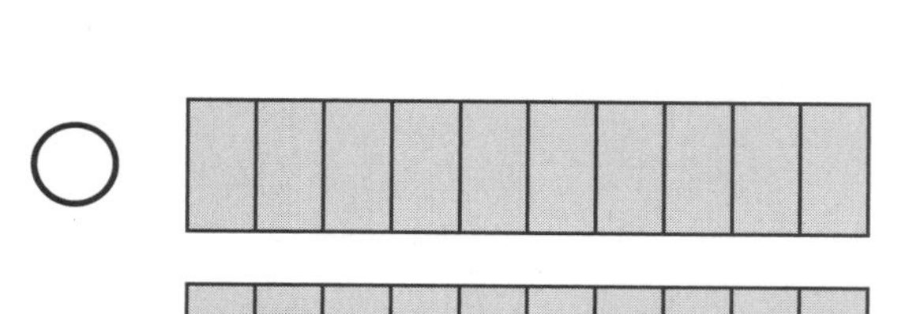

○ 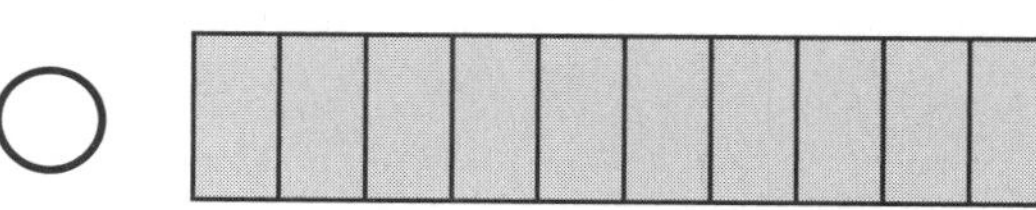

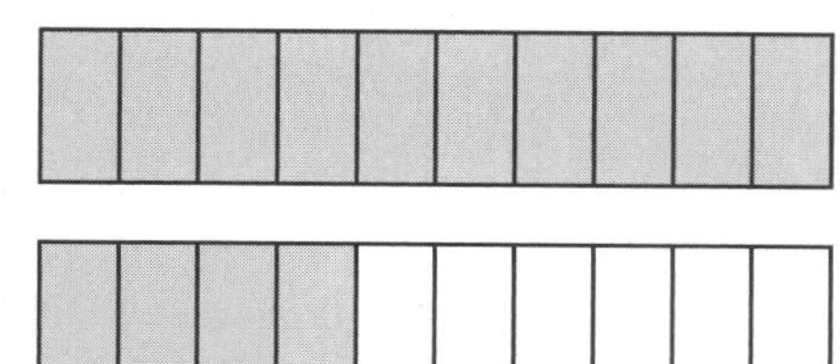

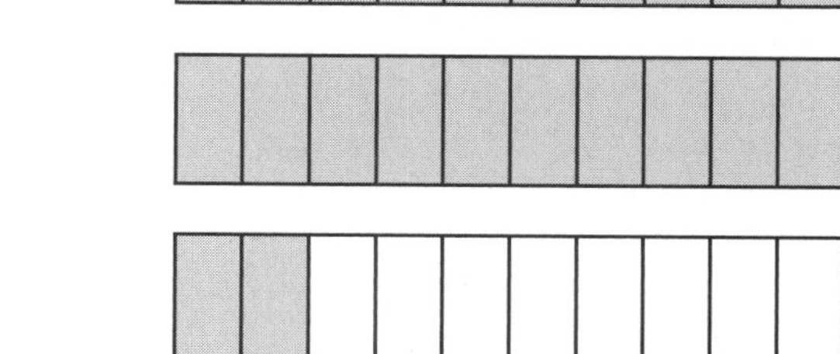

____

- - - - - - - - - - - - - - -

2 23, ______________, 25, 26

Directions Have students: 1 fill in the bubble next to the picture that shows the same number of shaded boxes as party hats; 2 write the missing number.

Name ____________________

Daily TEKS Review
7-1

1

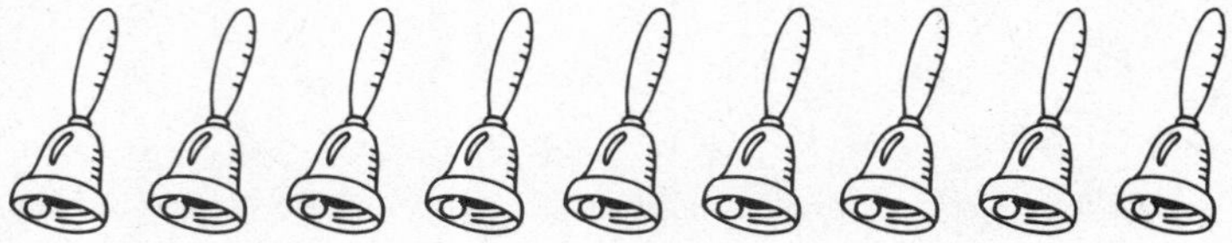

7 ○ 8 ○ 9 ○ 10 ○

2

○
○
○
○

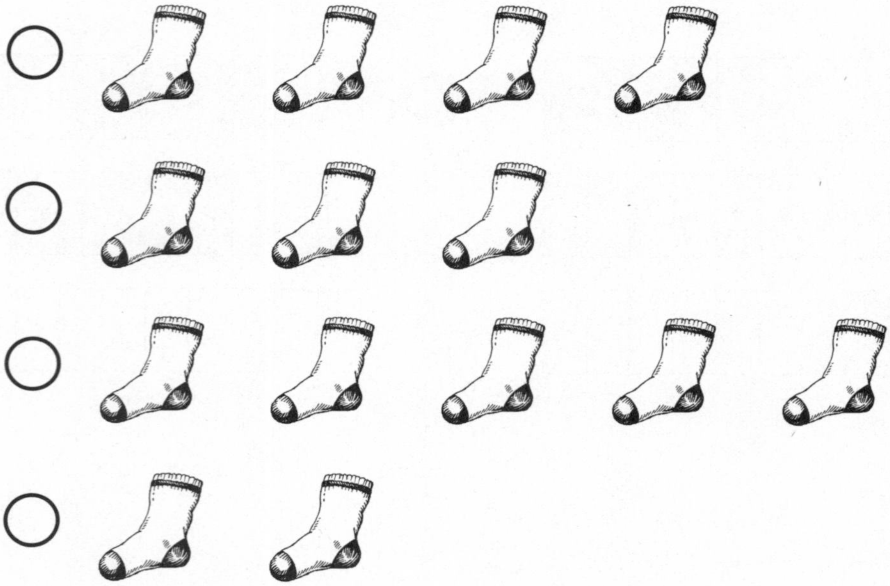

3

Directions Have students: 1 fill in the bubble below the number that tells how many bells; 2 fill in the bubble next to the picture that shows the same number of socks as shoes; 3 draw Xs on the cars to show 2 fewer.

Name ________________________________

Daily TEKS Review
7-2

○ 

○ 

○ 

○

2

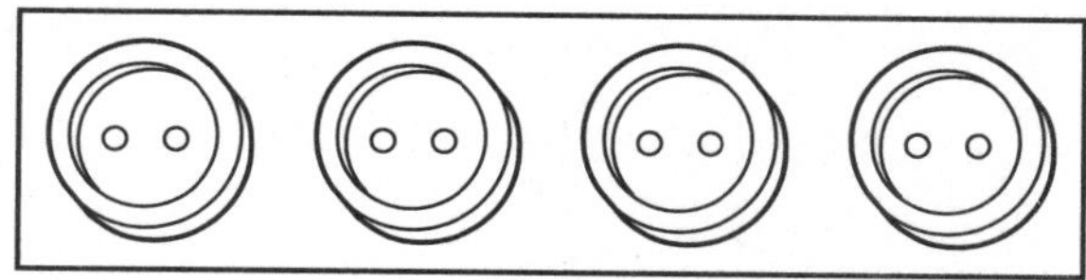

○ 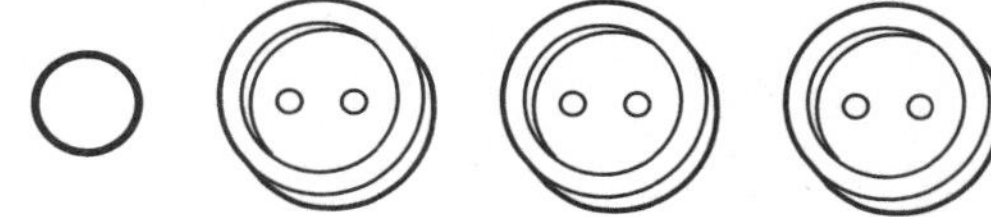

○ 

○ 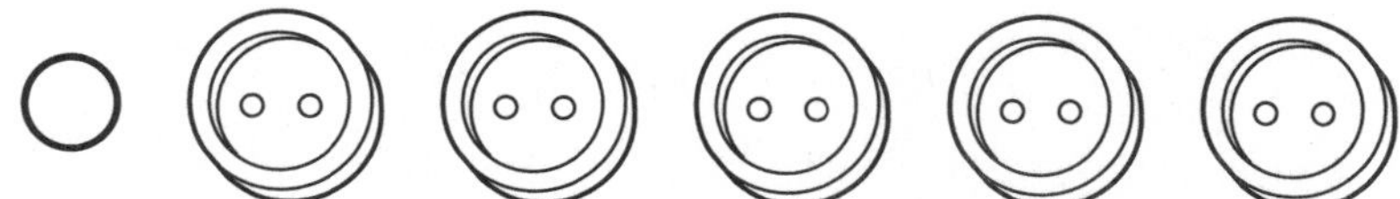

○ 

3

Directions Have students: 1 fill in the bubble next to the picture that shows 6 raindrops; 2 fill in the bubble next to the group with more buttons than the group in the box; 3 draw an X on a crab to show 1 fewer.

Name ______________________

Daily TEKS Review
7-3

○ 7

○ 6

○ 9

○ 8

2

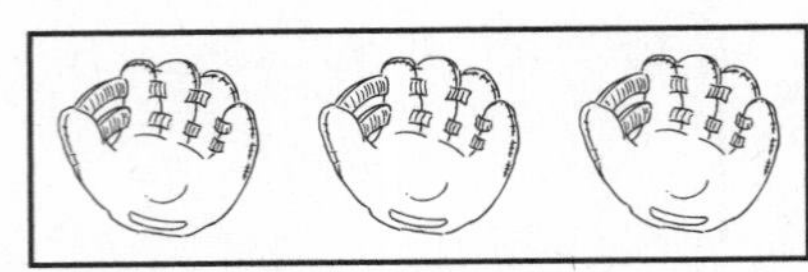

○ 

○ 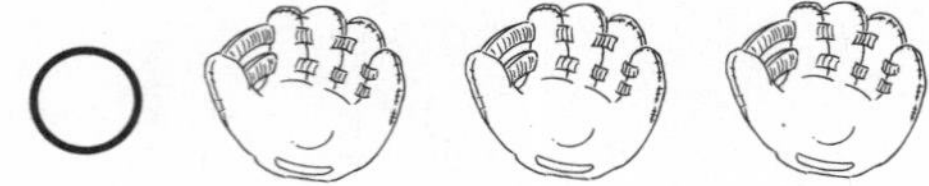

○ 

○ 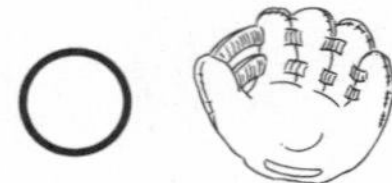

3

____

Directions Have students: 1 fill in the bubble next to the number that tells how many kangaroos; 2 fill in the bubble next to the group that shows 1 fewer mitt than the group in the box; 3 count the buses, and then write the number that tells how many.

Name ______________________

3 ○ 4 ○ 5 ○ 6 ○

______

______ in all.

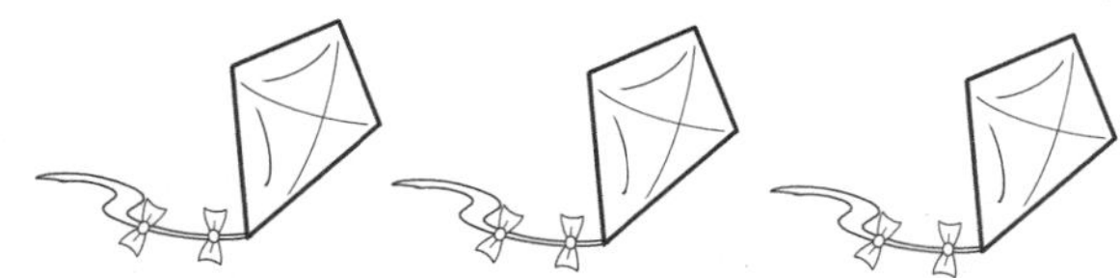

Directions Have students: 1 fill in the bubble below the number that tells how many soccer balls there are in all; 2 listen to the story, and then write the number that tells how many in all. *5 dogs are playing. 2 more join them. How many dogs are there in all?* 3 draw an X on a kite to show 1 fewer.

Name ______________________

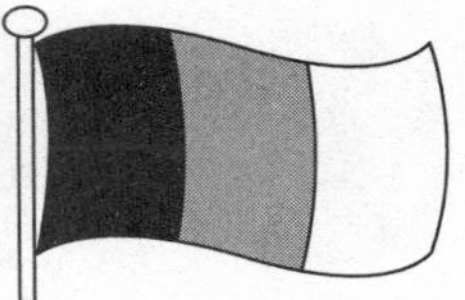

- ○ 0
- ○ 1
- ○ 3
- ○ 10

2

_______ + _______

3

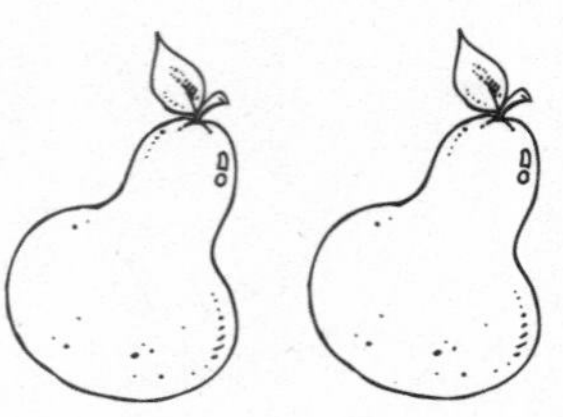

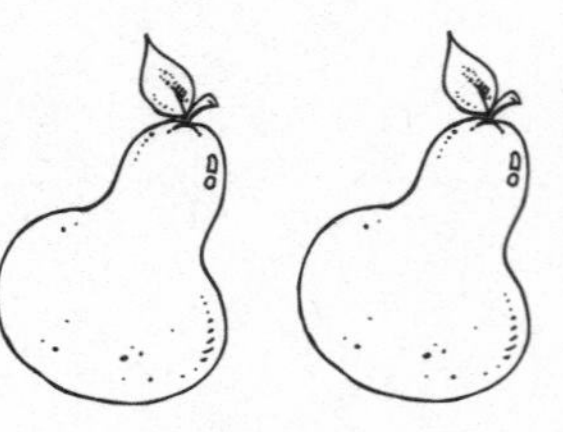

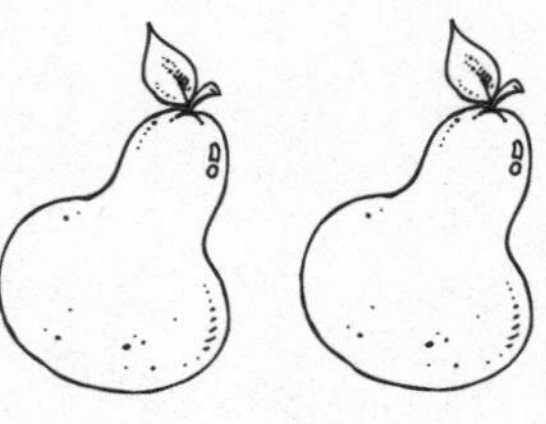

____

4 and 2 is _______.

Directions Have students: 1 fill in the bubble next to the number that tells how many stars there are on the flag; 2 write a number sentence to tell how many frogs are in the pond and how many frogs join them; 3 complete the sentence to tell how many in all.

Name ______________________________

Daily TEKS Review
7-6

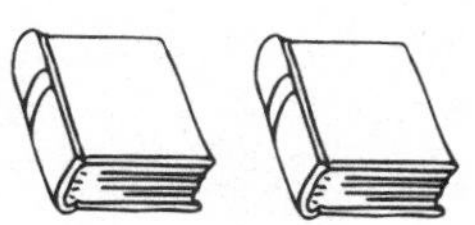

○ 2 + 2

○ 2 + 5

○ 5 + 5

○ 7 + 2

2

○ 

○ 

○ 

○ 

3

_______ + _______

Directions Have students: 1 fill in the bubble next to the number sentence that matches the picture; 2 fill in the bubble next to the group that shows more shells than the group in the box; 3 listen to the story, and then write a number sentence. *Sara has 3 beads on a string. She has 2 more beads on the table. How many beads does Sara have in all?*

Name ______________________________

1

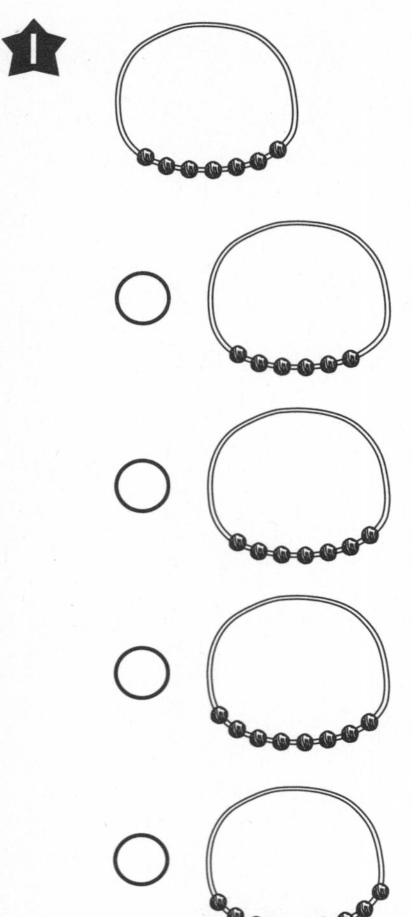

2

3

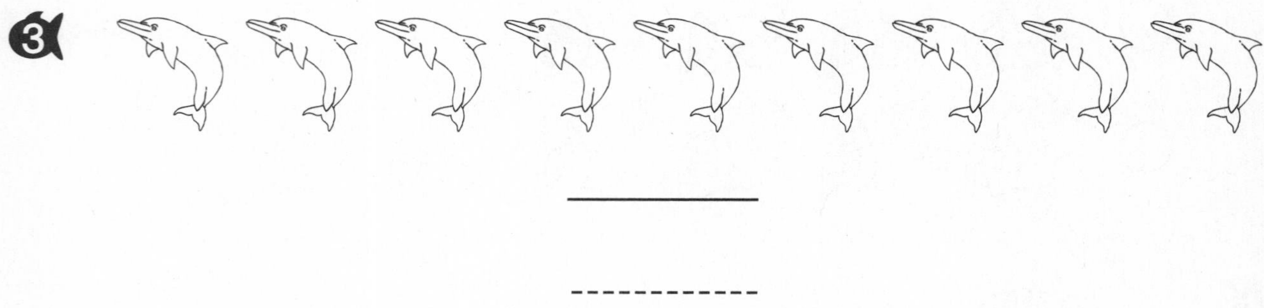

Directions Have students: 1 fill in the bubble next to the necklace with the same number of beads as the necklace at the top; 2 count the cows, and then write the number that tells how many; 3 count the dolphins, and then write the number that tells how many.

Name ______________________

Daily TEKS Review
7-8

1

○ 4 + 3 = 7
○ 4 + 2 = 6
○ 3 + 2 = 5
○ 2 + 3 = 5

2

8

○ 10

○ 9

○ 8

○ 7

3

________ + ________ = ________

Directions Have students: **1** fill in the bubble next to the addition sentence that tells how many planes there are in all; **2** fill in the bubble next to the number that is less than the number at the top; **3** write an addition sentence that tells how many flamingos there are in all.

Name ______________________

Daily TEKS Review
8-1

○ 2 and 2 is 4.

○ 2 and 1 is 3.

○ 3 and 1 is 5.

○ 3 and 1 is 4.

2

○ 

○ 

○ 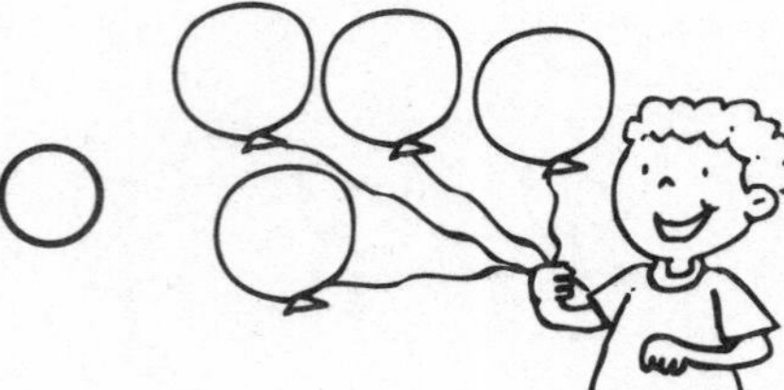

○ 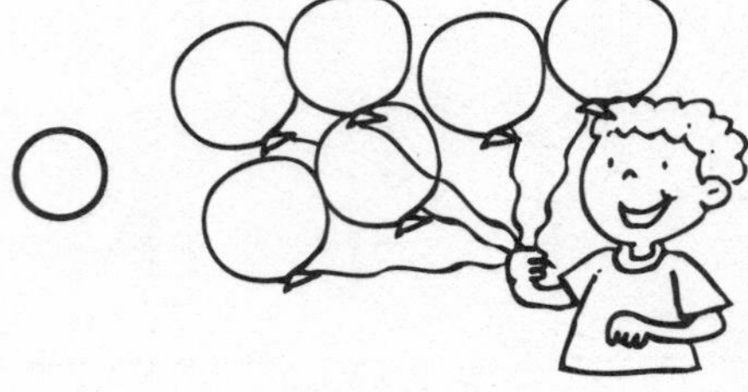

3

1, 2, ______, 4, 5, 6, ______, 8, 9, ______

Directions Have students: 1 fill in the bubble next to the sentence that matches the picture; 2 fill in the bubble next to the picture that shows the boy with 2 more balloons than the girl; 3 write the missing numbers.

Name ______________________

Daily TEKS Review
8-2

1

○ 7 − 6

○ 5 − 1

○ 6 − 5

○ 6 − 1

2 5 take away 2 is ___.

○ 7

○ 5

○ 3

○ 2

3

Directions Have students: 1 fill in the bubble next to the number sentence that matches the picture; 2 fill in the bubble next to the number that completes the sentence; 3 draw groups of counters to show 2 ways to make 5.

Name ______________________

$3 + 3 = \underline{?}$

○ 2

○ 4

○ 6

○ 8

2

○ $4 + 4 = 8$

○ $3 + 3 = 6$

○ $4 + 3 = 7$

○ $5 + 2 = 7$

3

______ ______ ______

______ and ______ is ______.

Directions Have students: 1 fill in the bubble next to the number that completes the addition sentence; 2 fill in the bubble next to the addition sentence that matches the picture; 3 complete the sentence that tells about joining the groups of penguins.

Name ______________________________

Daily TEKS Review
8-4

○ 0 more

○ 1 more

○ 2 more

○ 3 more

2

○ 7

○ 6

○ 3

○ 1

3

______ ______ ______

______ take away ______ is ______.

Directions Have students: 1 fill in the bubble next to the number that tells how many more bones there are than dogs; 2 fill in the bubble next to the number that tells how many lemons are left on the tree; 3 complete the sentence that matches the picture.

Name ______________________________

○ 4 − 3

○ 4 − 1

○ 3 − 3

○ 3 − 1

2

○ 

○ 

○ 

○ 

3

6 take away 4 is 2.

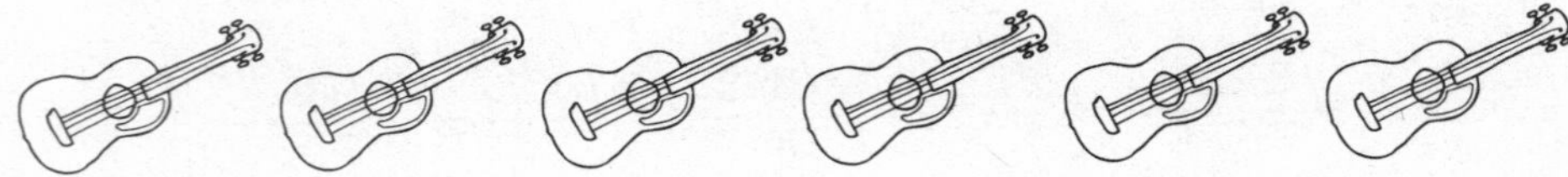

Directions Have students: 1 fill in the bubble next to the subtraction that matches the picture; 2 fill in the bubble next to the picture that shows a way to make 10; 3 draw Xs on the guitars to match the sentence.

Name ______________________

Daily TEKS Review
8-6

1 $5 + 1 =$ ____

- ◯ 2
- ◯ 4
- ◯ 6
- ◯ 8

2

- ◯ 10
- ◯ 9
- ◯ 1
- ◯ 0

3

____

Directions Have students: **1** fill in the bubble next to the number that completes the addition sentence; **2** fill in the bubble next to the number that tells how many eggs are in the nest; **3** color the leaves to show a group with 2 fewer, and then write the number that tells how many.

Name ________________________________

○ $3 + 2 = 5$ ○ $4 + 4 = 8$

○ $4 + 3 = 7$ ○ $4 + 2 = 6$

2

○ 10

○ 7

○ 4

○ 3

3

Directions Have students: 1 fill in the bubble next to the addition sentence that matches the picture; 2 fill in the bubble next to the number that tells how many flowers are left; 3 color the shirts in 2 colors to show a way to make 5.

Name ____________________

Daily TEKS Review
8-8

○ 3

○ 4

○ 5

○ 6

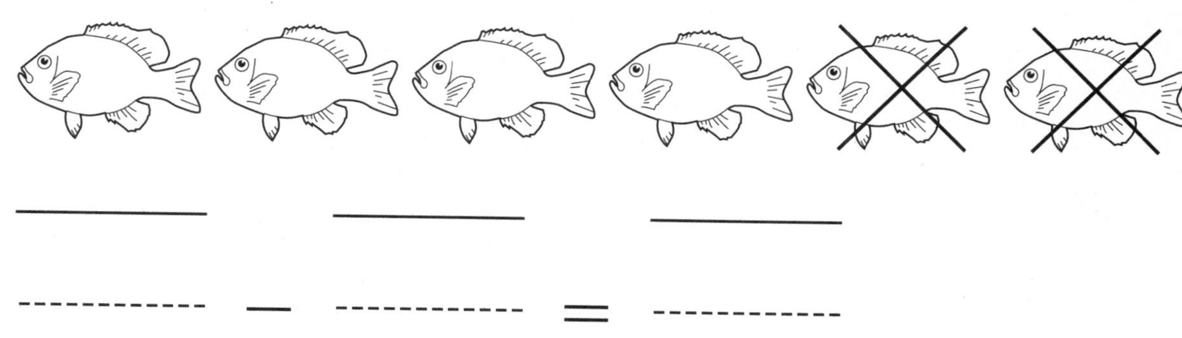

______ − ______ = ______

Directions Have students: 1 fill in the bubble next to the number that tells how many children are in line; 2 write a subtraction sentence that matches the picture.

Name ______________________

1

9 ○ 10 ○ 12 ○ 20 ○

2

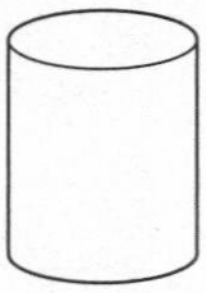

○  ○

○ 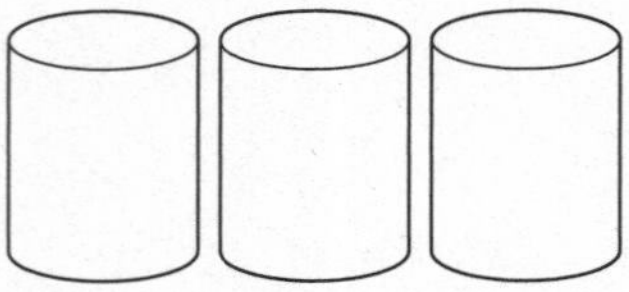 ○

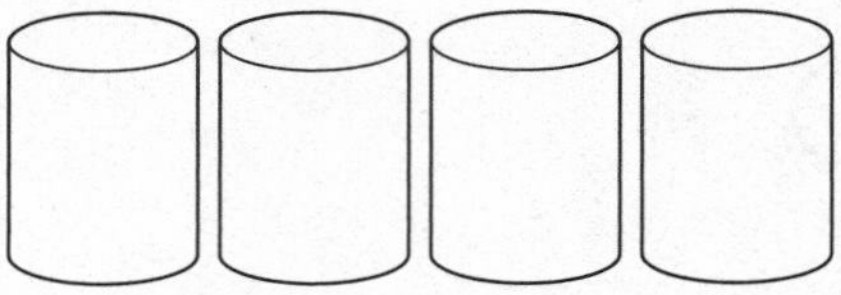

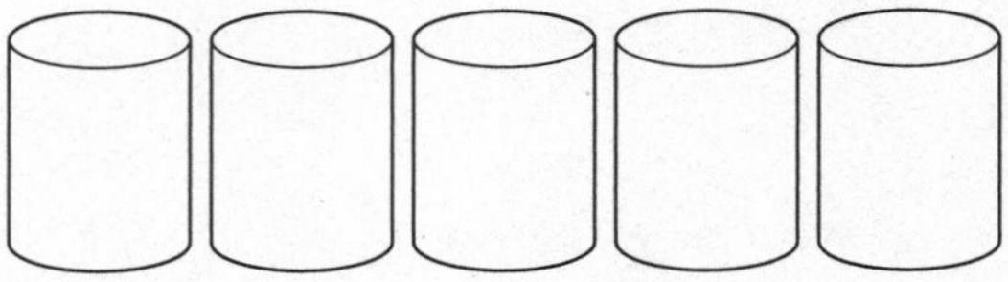

3

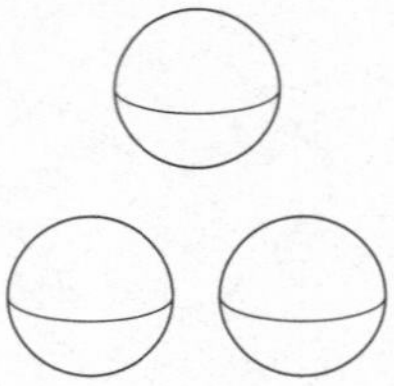

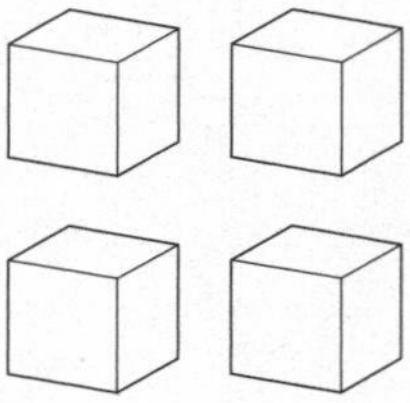

_____ + _____ = _____

Directions Have students: 1 fill in the bubble below the number that tells how many paintbrushes; 2 fill in the bubble next to the group that shows 2 more blocks than at the top; 3 write the numbers that tell how many of each block, and then write the sum to complete the addition sentence.

Name ______________________

Daily TEKS Review
9-2

1 64

70 ○ 66 ○ 65 ○ 60 ○

2

○ 

○ 

○ 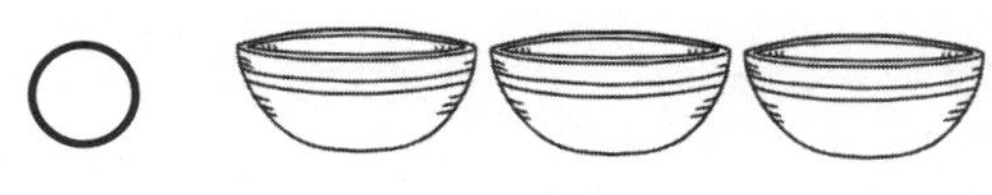

○ 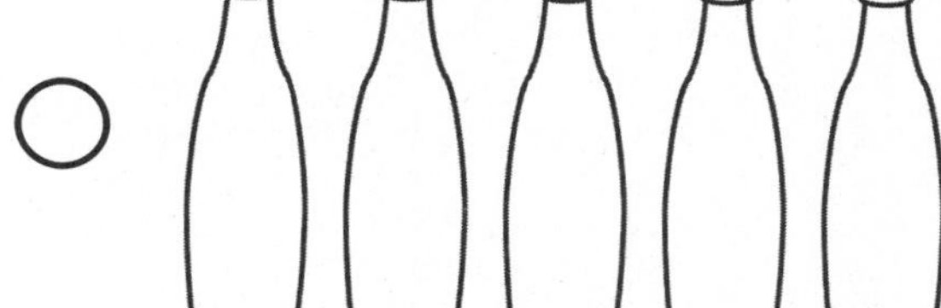

3

●	●	●	●	●

______

Directions Have students: 1 fill in the bubble below the number that is 1 more than 64; 2 fill in the bubble next to the group that has the fewest; 3 draw more counters to show eight in all, and then write the number that tells how many.

Name ______________________

1

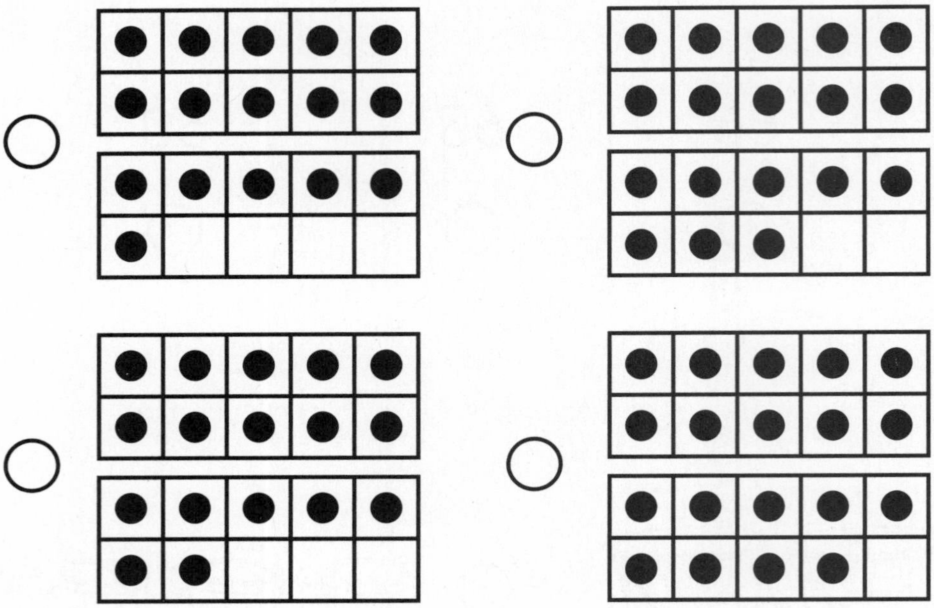

2 7

0	5	7	9
○	○	○	○

3

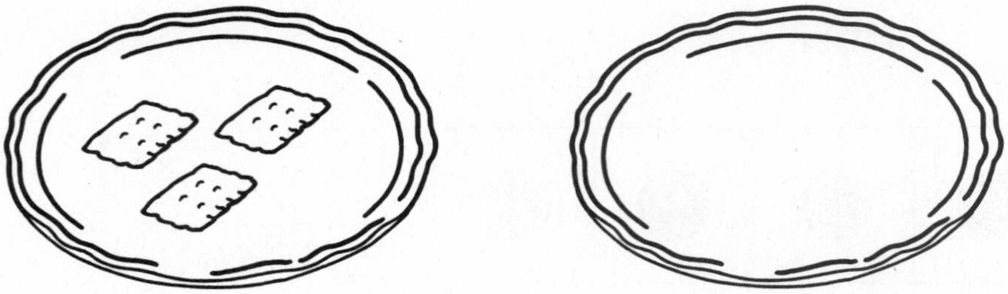

_____ + _____ = _____

Directions Have students: 1 fill in the bubble next to the set that shows 19; 2 fill in the bubble below the number that is greater than 7; 3 draw 4 crackers on the empty plate, and then write an addition sentence that tells how many crackers there are in all.

Name ____________________

Daily TEKS Review
9-4

1

○ 4 + 3

○ 3 + 6

○ 3 + 3

○ 3 + 5

2

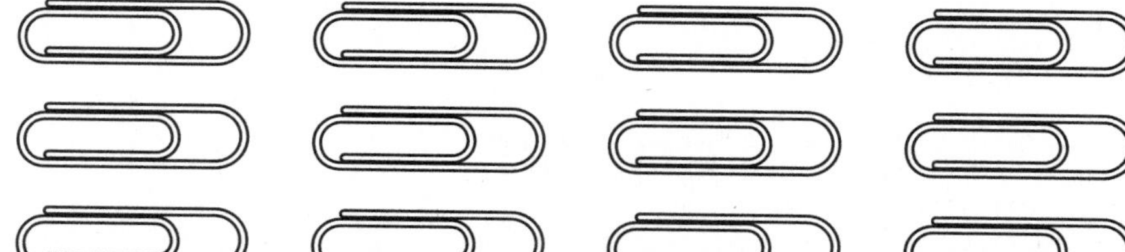

9	10	11	12
○	○	○	○

3

____

Directions Have students: 1 fill in the bubble next to the numbers that show joining the 2 groups of boats; 2 fill in the bubble below the number that tells how many stars; 3 count the paper clips, and then write the number that tells how many.

Name ______________________________

1 $2 + 4$

○ 

○ 

○ 

○ 

2 

○ 9

○ 7

○ 8

○ 6

3

50, 51, __________, 53, 54, __________,

56, 57, __________, 59, 60

Directions Have students: 1 fill in the bubble next to the picture that matches 2 + 4; 2 fill in the bubble next to the number that tells how many shapes there are; 3 count from 50 to 60 and write the missing numbers.

Name ______________________

○ 4 + 2 = 6

○ 2 + 5 = 7

○ 3 + 4 = 7

○ 5 + 5 = 10

2

○ 2

○ 3

○ 4

○ 5

3

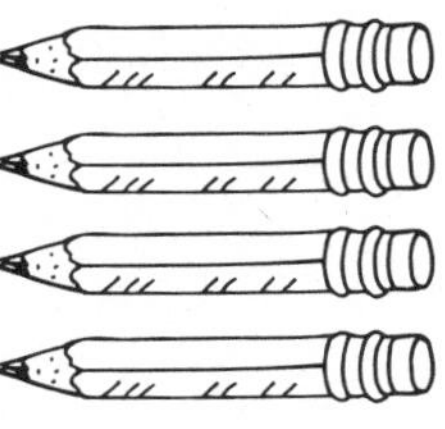

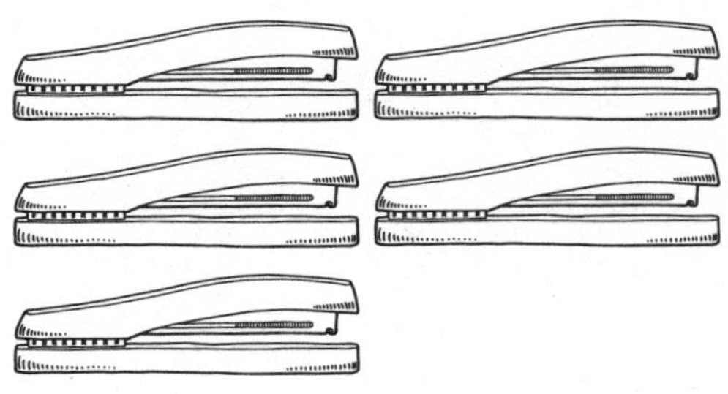

______ + ______ = ______

Directions Have students: **1** fill in the bubble next to the addition sentence that matches the picture; **2** listen to the story, and then fill in the bubble next to the number that tells how many soccer balls are left. Say: *Jill has 9 soccer balls but kicks 5 balls away. How many balls are left?* **3** write an addition sentence that matches the picture.

Name ___________________________

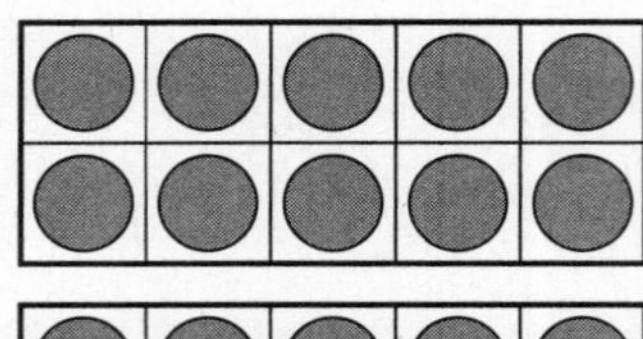

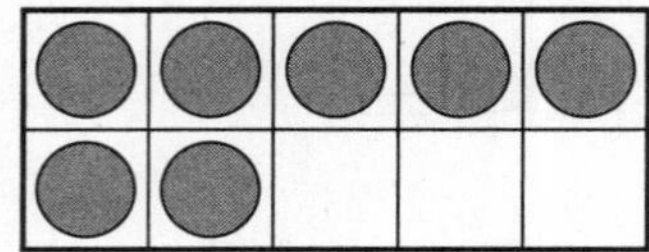

○ 7

○ 12

○ 15

○ 17

2

Directions Have students: 1 fill in the bubble next to the number that tells how many counters; 2 draw a group of teddy bears that has 1 fewer than the group shown.

Name ______________________________

Daily TEKS Review
10-2

1

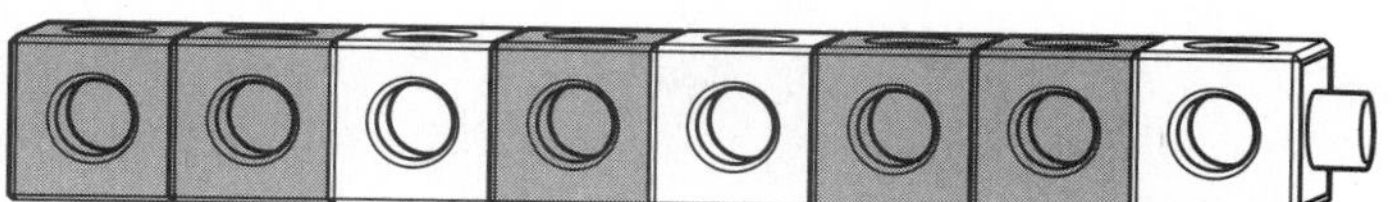

○ 2 ○ 5

○ 3 ○ 8

2

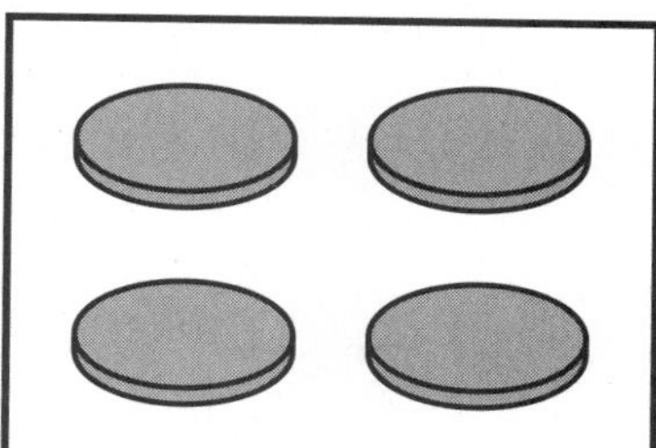

○ $2 + 3 = 5$ ○ $1 + 3 = 4$

○ $0 + 5 = 5$ ○ $1 + 4 = 5$

3

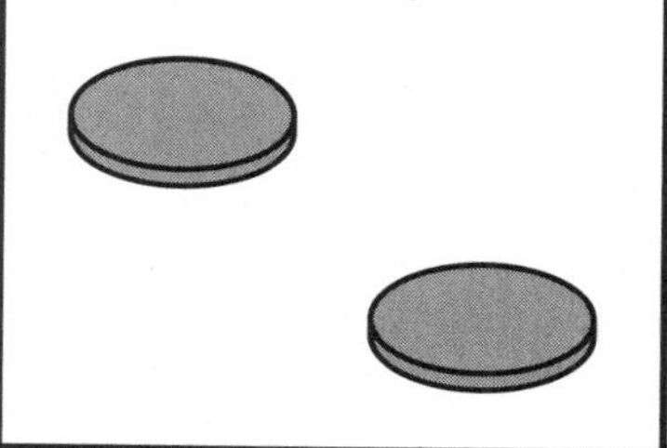

________ + ________ = ________

Directions Have students: 1 fill in the bubble next to the number that tells how many white cubes are in the cube train; 2 fill in the bubble next to the number sentence that tells about joining the 2 groups of counters; 3 write a number sentence that tells about joining the 2 groups of counters.

Name ________________________________

Daily TEKS Review
10-3

1 $4 + 1 = 5$

○ 

○ 

○ 

○ 

2

______ ______ ______

------ + ------ = ------

______ ______ ______

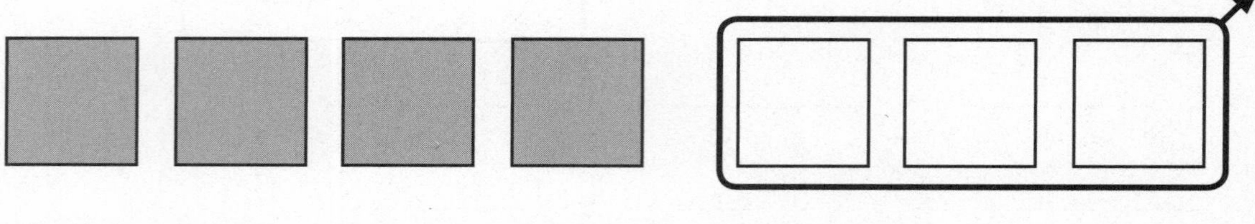

______ ______ ______

------ − ------ = ------

______ ______ ______

Directions Have students: **1** fill in the bubble next to the picture that matches the number sentence; **2** write the numbers that complete these related facts.

Name ____________________

Daily TEKS Review
10-4

1

○ $6 + 2 = 8$ ○ $2 + 6 = 8$

○ $6 - 2 = 4$ ○ $4 + 2 = 6$

2

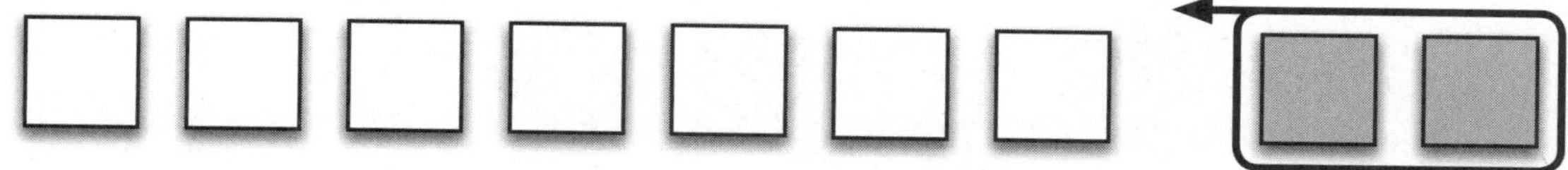

○ $7 - 2 = 5$ ○ $9 - 2 = 7$

○ $7 + 2 = 9$ ○ $6 + 3 = 9$

3

_____ + _____ = _____

_____ − _____ = _____

Directions Have students: 1 fill in the bubble next to the subtraction sentence; 2 fill in the bubble next to the number sentence that matches the picture; 3 write the numbers that complete these related facts.

Name ______________________

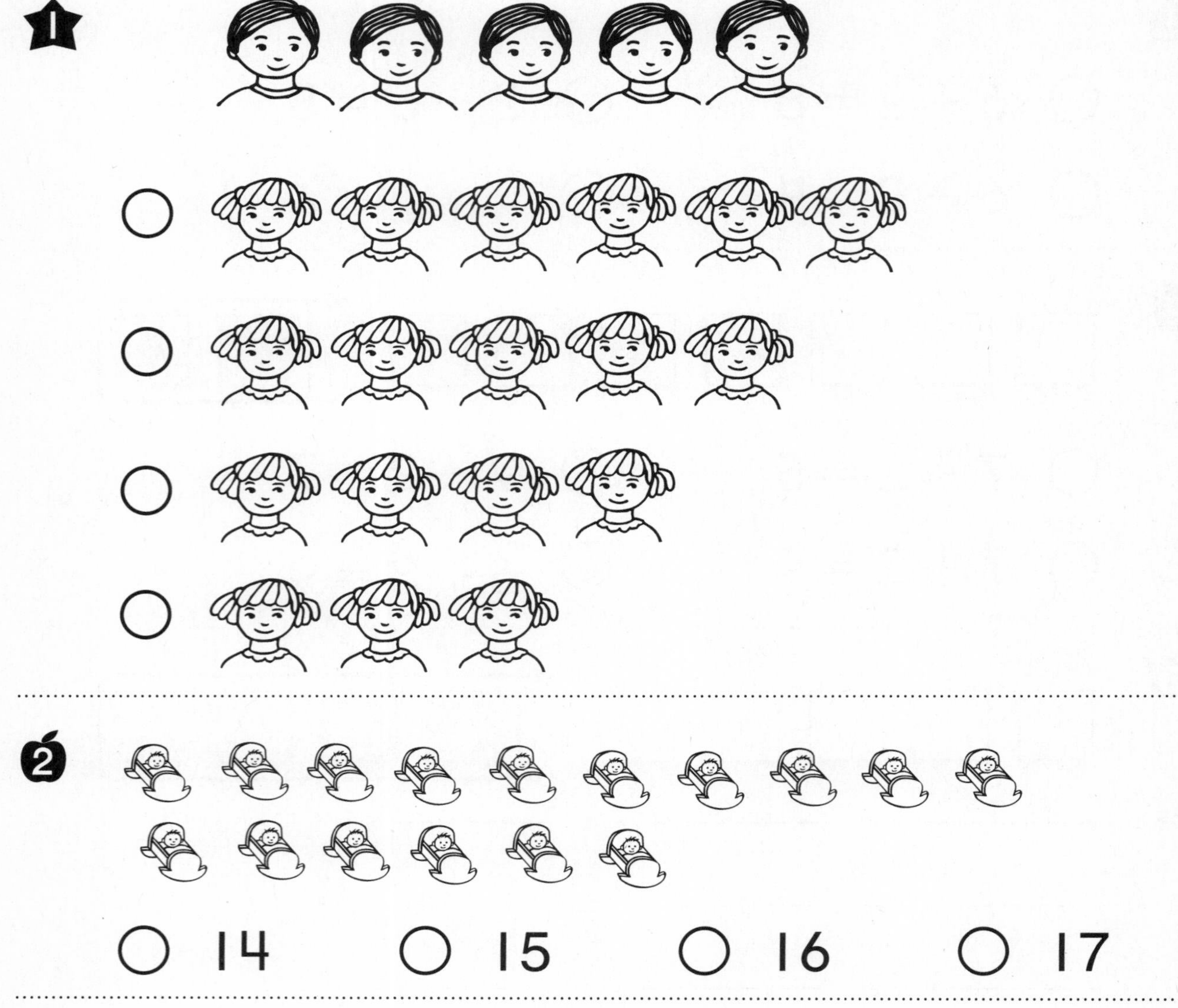

○ 14 ○ 15 ○ 16 ○ 17

Directions Have students: 1 fill in the bubble next to the picture that shows the same number of girls as boys; 2 fill in the bubble next to the number that tells how many babies; 3 count the number of children swinging, and then practice writing the number two times.

Name ____________________

Daily TEKS Review
10-6

○ 

○ 

○

○ 

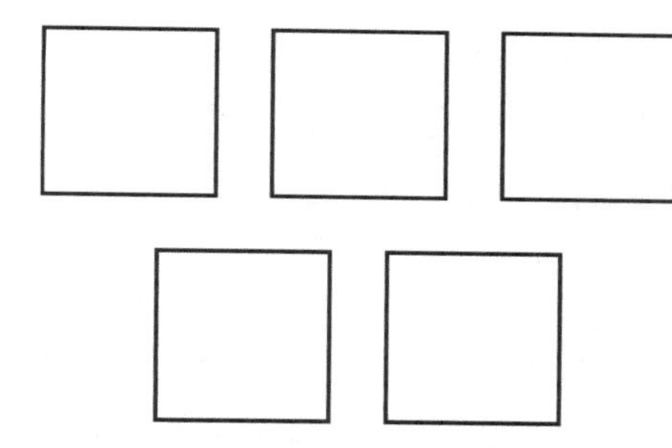

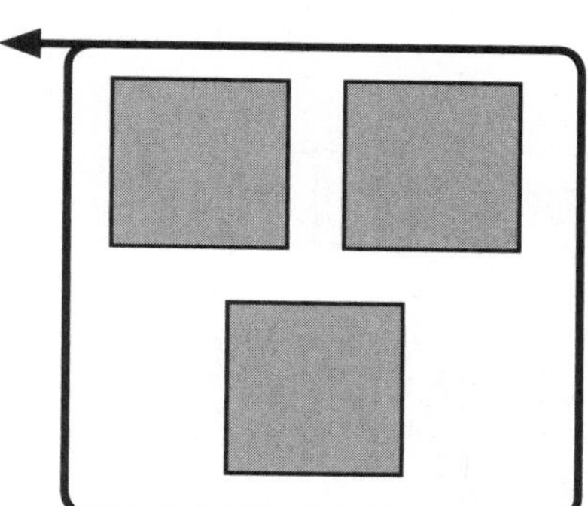

$7 + 1 = 8$

$2 + 6 = 8$

$5 + 4 = 9$

$5 + 3 = 8$

Directions Have students: 1 fill in the bubble next to the picture that shows 7 shapes; 2 circle the number sentence that matches the picture.

Name ______________________________

Daily TEKS Review
10-7

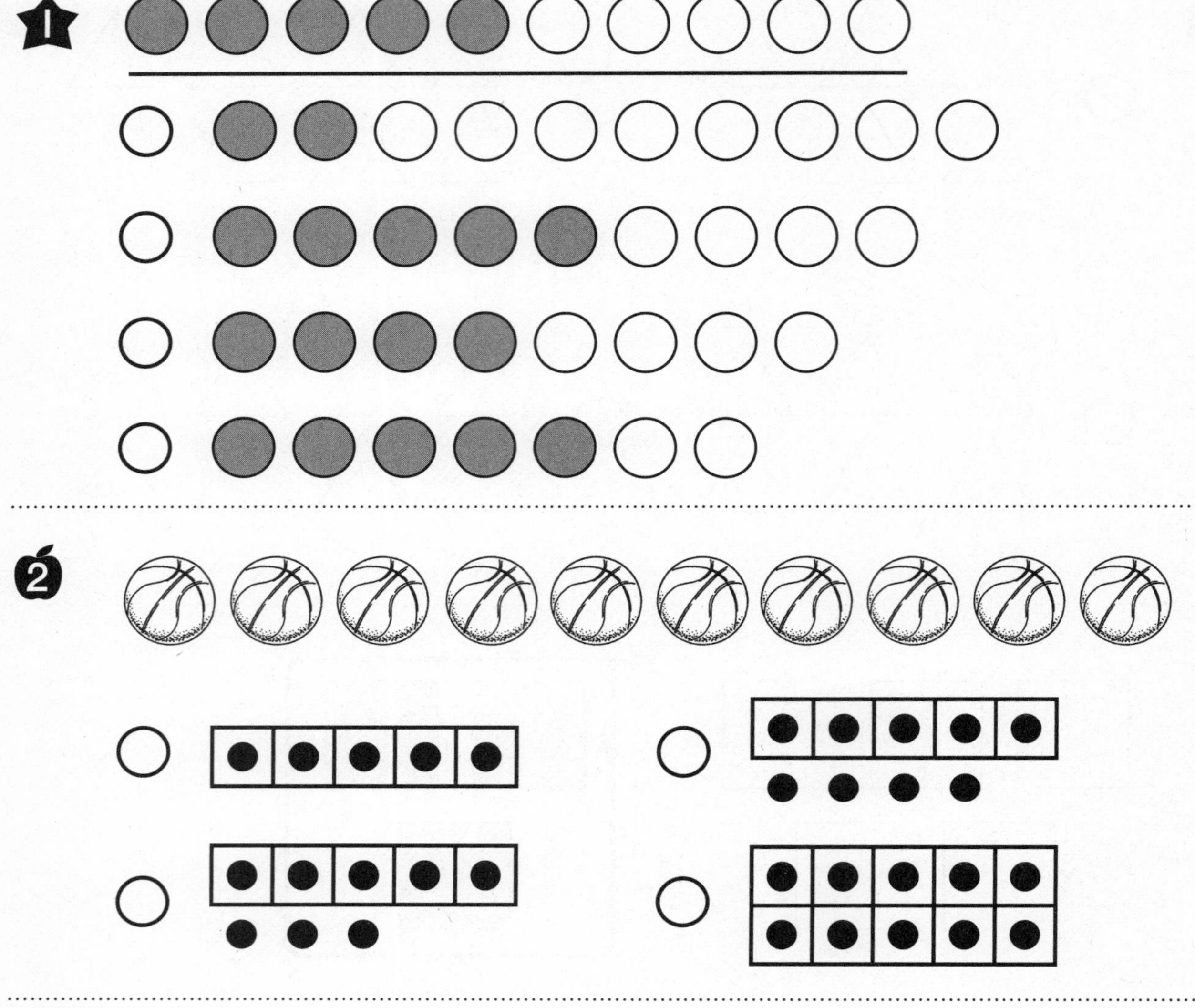

3

______

______

______

______

Directions Have students: 1 fill in the bubble next to the picture that shows another way to make 10; 2 fill in the bubble next to the picture that shows how many basketballs; 3 count the toys, and then write the numbers that tell how many.

Name ______________________

Daily TEKS Review
11-1

○ 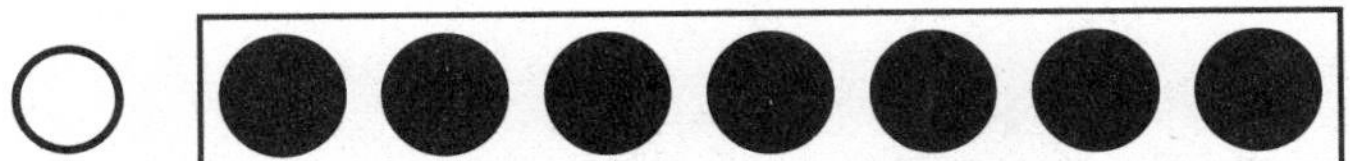

○ 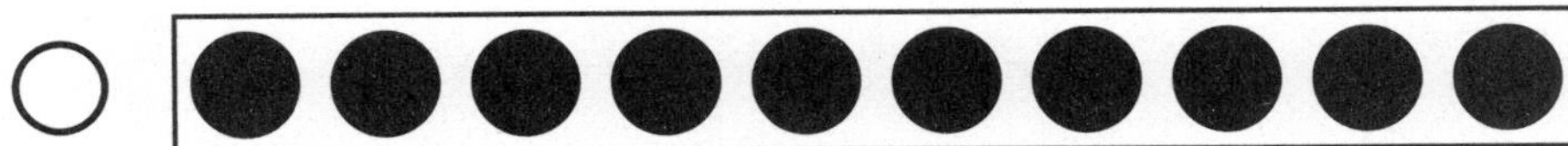

○ 

○

2

○ 

○ 

○ 

○ 

3

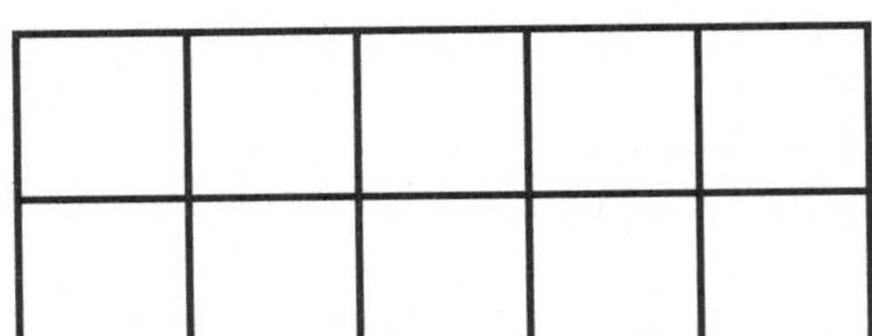

13

Directions Have students: 1 fill in the bubble next to the picture that shows a group that has fewer than 10 counters; 2 fill in the bubble next to the group that shows 2 fewer chicks than the group at the top; 3 draw counters to show the number.

Name ______________________

1

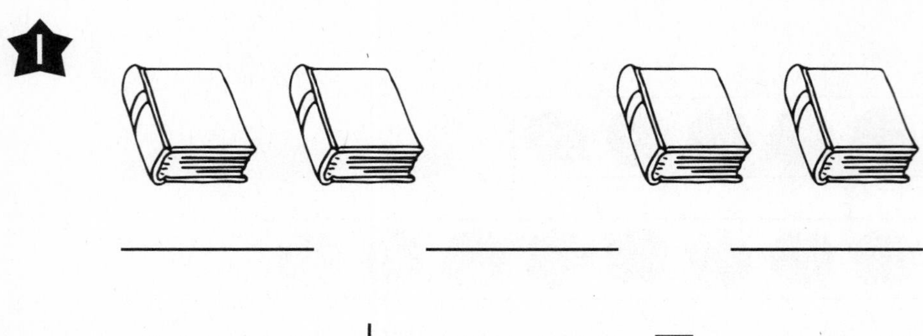

______ ______ ______

______ + ______ = ______

______ ______ ______

2

○

○

○

○

3

______

Directions Have students: 1 write a number sentence that tells about joining the 2 groups of books; 2 fill in the bubble next to the group that shows 1 fewer cat than the group at the top; 3 draw nine counters and write the number.

Name ______________________________

Daily TEKS Review
11-3

1 4 and 4 is 8.

○ 

○ 

○ 

○ 

2

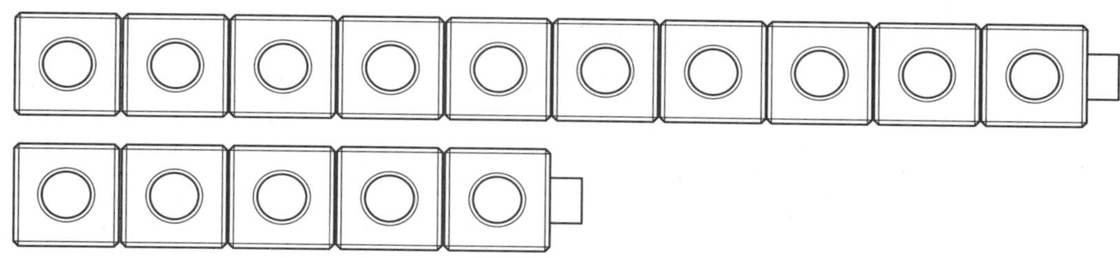

○ 10

○ 15

○ 19

○ 20

1	2	3	4	5	6	7	8	9	10
11	12	13	14	15	16	17	18	19	20
21	22	23	24	25	26	27	28	29	30
31	32	33	34	35	36	37	38	39	40
41	42	43	44	45	46	47	48	49	50

Directions Have students: **1** fill in the bubble next to the picture that matches the number sentence; **2** fill in the bubble next to the number that tells how many cubes; **3** circle the numbers they would say if they started at 10 and counted by 10s.

Name ____________________

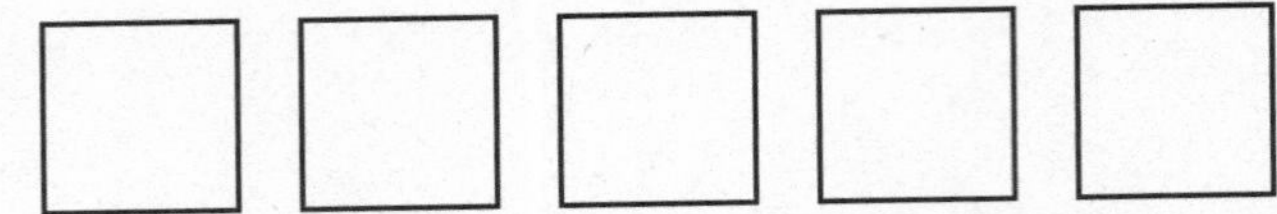

○ 10 = 5 + 5
10 = 8 + 2

○ 10 = 7 + 3
10 = 3 + 7

○ 9 = 5 + 4
9 = 4 + 5

○ 10 = 6 + 4
10 = 4 + 6

2

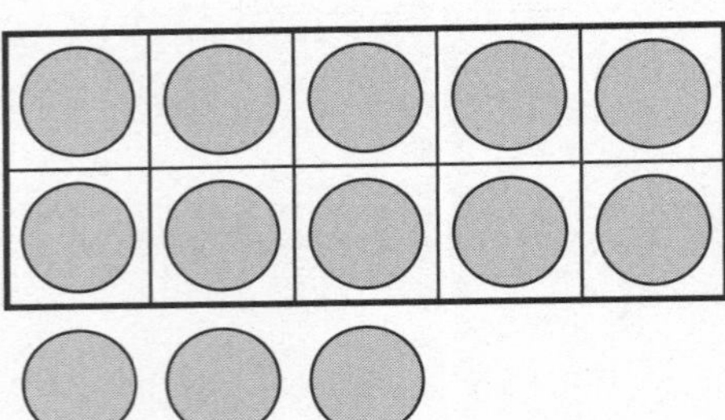

______

Directions Have students: 1 fill in the bubble next to the related facts that match the picture; 2 count the counters, and then write the number that tells how many.

Name ____________________

Daily TEKS Review
11-5

○ 5
○ 40
○ 50
○ 55

2

○ 5
○ 6
○ 7
○ 8

3

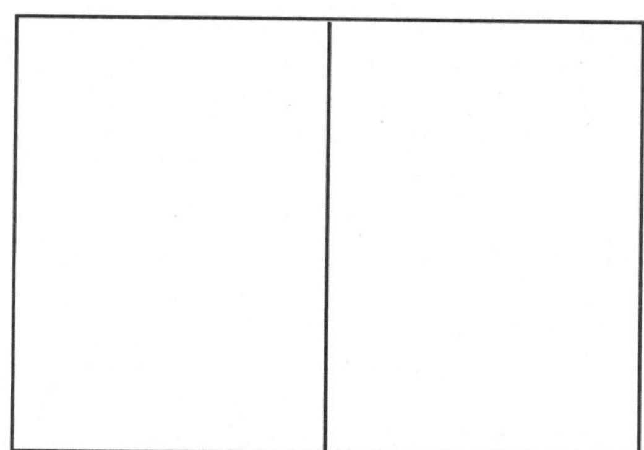

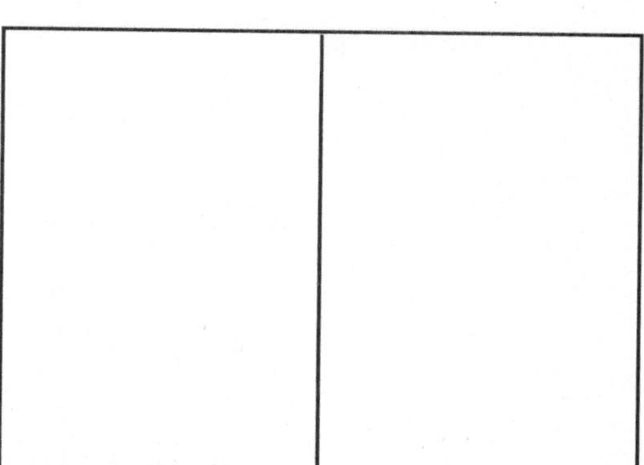

Directions Have students: 1 fill in the bubble next to the number that tells how many cubes; 2 fill in the bubble next to the number that tells how many books; 3 use counters, then draw two different ways to make 10 in two parts.

Name ______________________________

Daily TEKS Review
12-1

  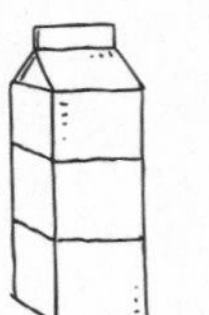 

○ $4 + 3 = 7$

○ $3 + 3 = 6$

○ $1 + 2 = 3$

○ $3 + 2 = 5$

 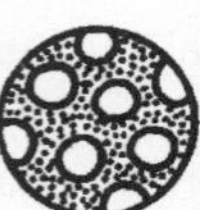  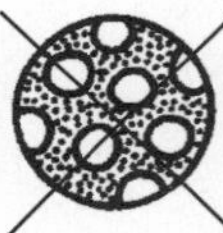 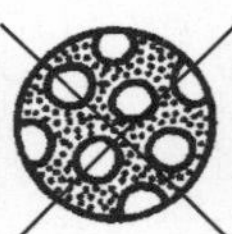 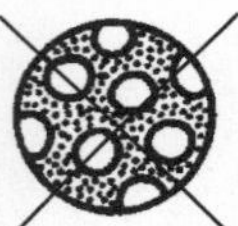

____

Directions Have students: 1 fill in the bubble next to the addition sentence that tells about joining the 2 groups of milk; 2 write the number that tells how many marbles are left.

Name ______________________

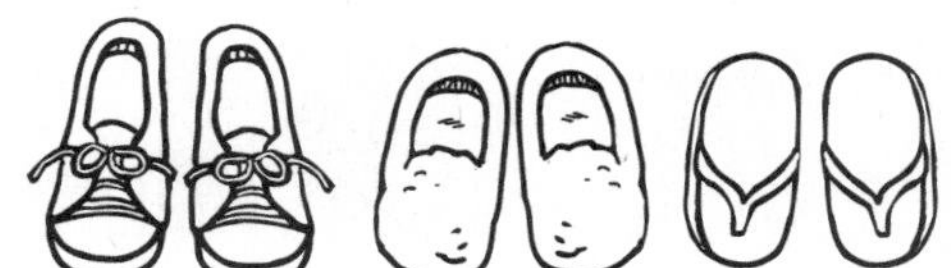

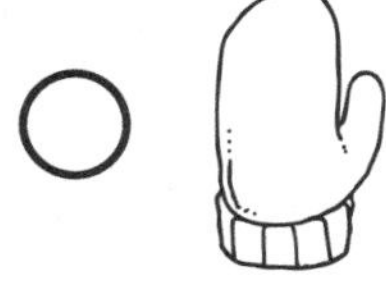

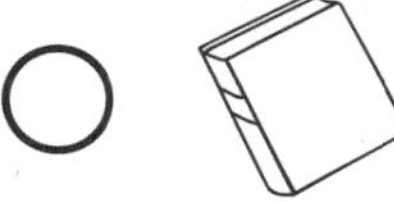

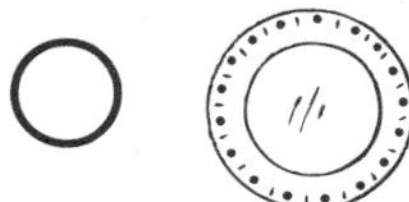

Directions Have students: 1 fill in the bubble next to the picture that shows the object that belongs in the group; 2 fill in the bubble next to the picture that shows the object that is a different shape from the others; 3 draw a picture to show the objects sorted by shape.

Name ______________________________

Daily TEKS Review
12-3

1

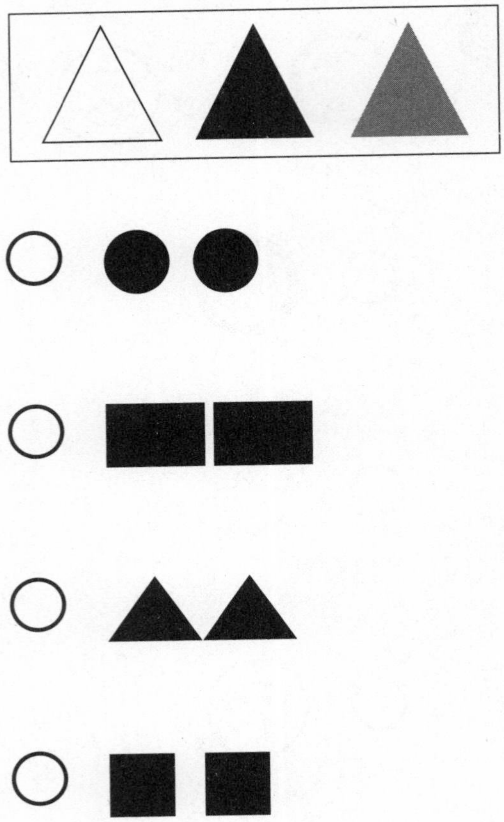

○

○

○

○

2

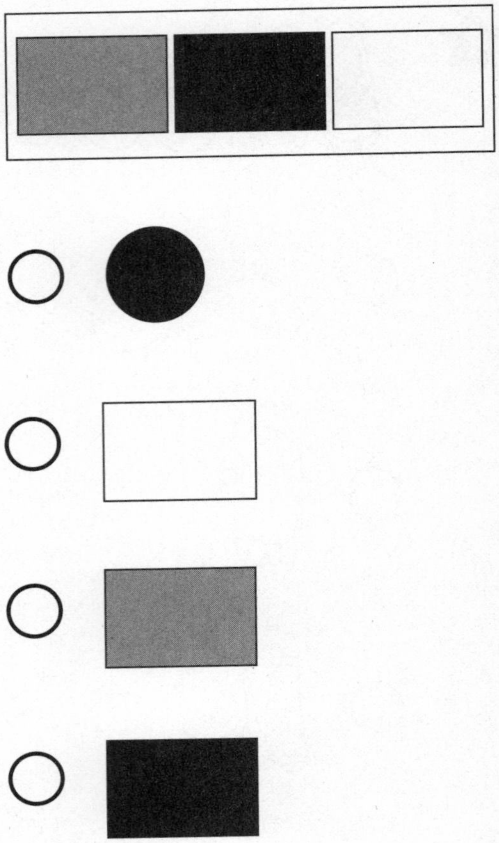

○

○

○

○

3

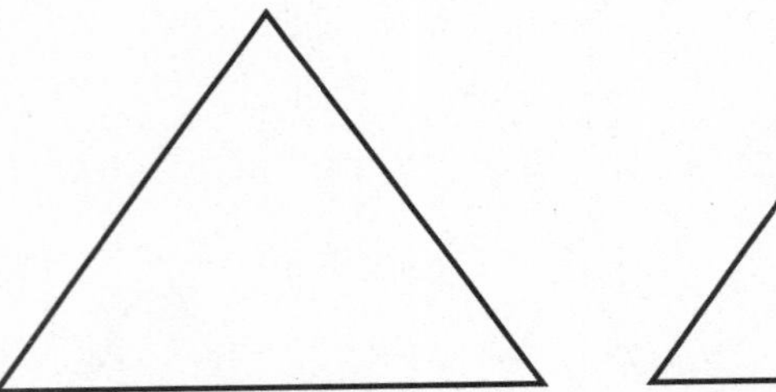

Directions Have students: 1 fill in the bubble next to the picture that shows shapes that belong in the group at the top; 2 fill in the bubble next to the picture of the shape that does **not** belong with the sorted shapes; 3 draw 2 more shapes that belong in the group.

Name ______________________

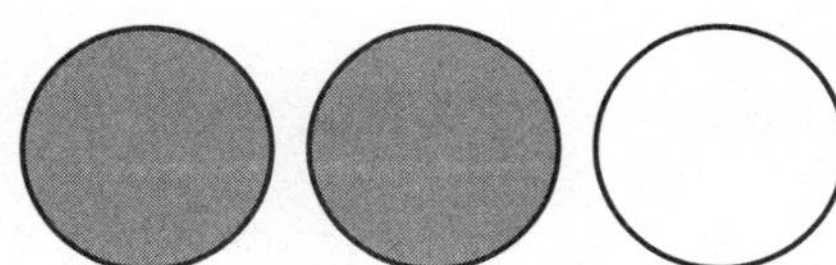

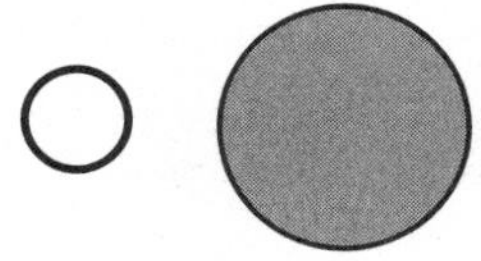

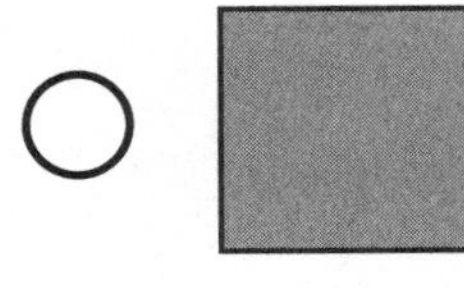

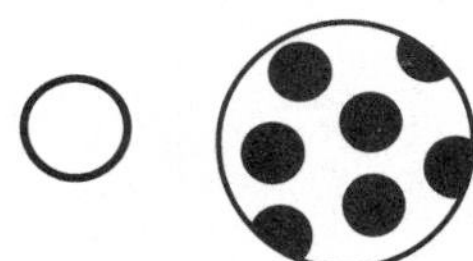

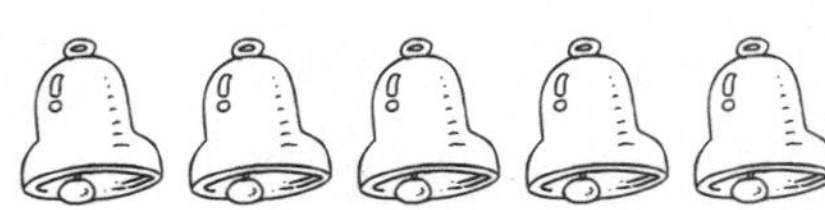

○ 2

○ 3

○ 4

○ 5

Directions Have students: 1 fill in the bubble next to the shape that does **not** belong in the group at the top; 2 fill in the bubble next to the number that tells how many bells; 3 draw 6 birds in the tree.

Name ______________________________

Daily TEKS Review
12-5

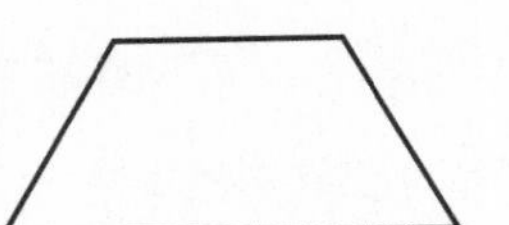

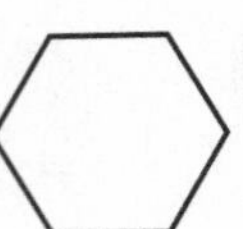

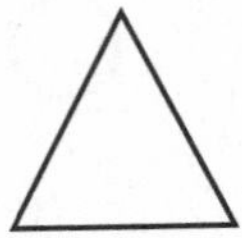

○ 

○ 

○ 

○ 

3 $10 - \underline{\quad ? \quad} = 4$

$10 - 4 = \underline{\quad ? \quad}$

○ 3

○ 5

○ 6

○ 8

Directions Have students: 1 circle the triangle; 2 fill in the bubble next to the picture that shows a group of 6 hearts; 3 fill in the bubble next to the number that completes the related facts.

Name ______________________

Daily TEKS Review
12-6

$4 + 5 = ?$

- ○ 1
- ○ 4
- ○ 5
- ○ 9

- ○ 2
- ○ 3
- ○ 4
- ○ 5

______

$4 + 1 =$ ______

Directions Have students: fill in the bubble next to the sum of the addition sentence; fill in the bubble next to the number that tells how many birds are left; write the number that completes the addition sentence.

Name ______________________________

1

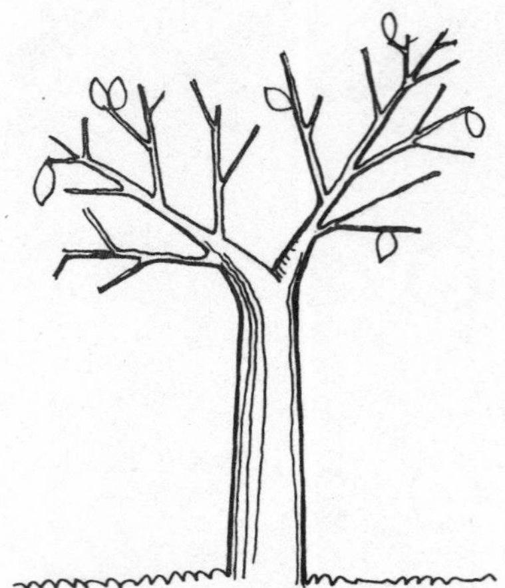

- ○ 4
- ○ 5
- ○ 6
- ○ 7

2

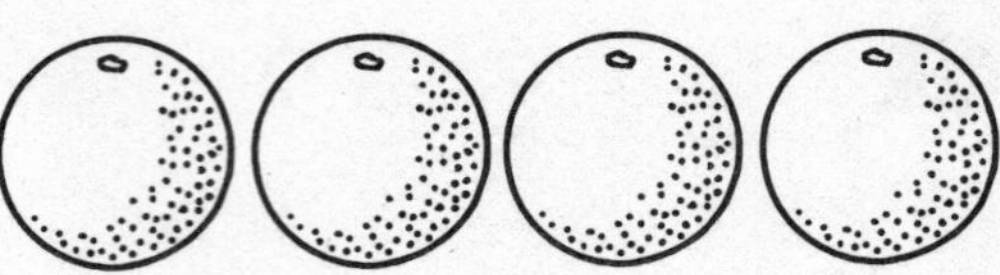

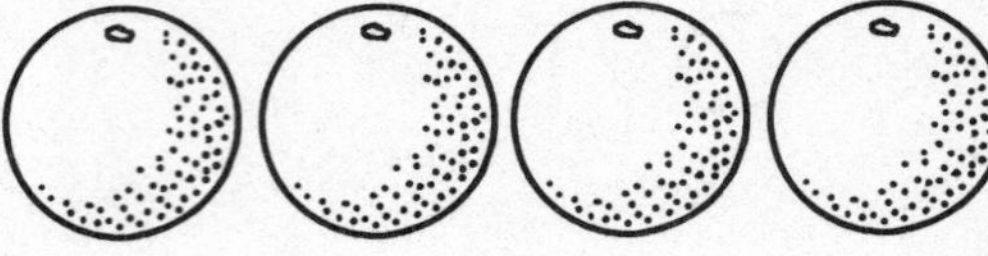

- ○ $4 + 4 = 8$
- ○ $8 - 4 = 4$
- ○ $5 + 5 = 10$
- ○ $4 + 5 = 9$

3 $7 - 3 = 4$

____ + 3 = ____

Directions Have students: 1 fill in the bubble next to the number that tells how many leaves are left on the tree if 2 leaves fall off; 2 fill in the bubble next to the number sentence that tells about joining the 2 groups of oranges; 3 write the numbers to complete the related fact.

Name ____________________

○ 4

○ 3

○ 2

○ 1

Directions Have students: 1 fill in the bubble next to the number that tells how many frogs are left on the log; 2 circle the set with fewer shells.

Name ______________________________

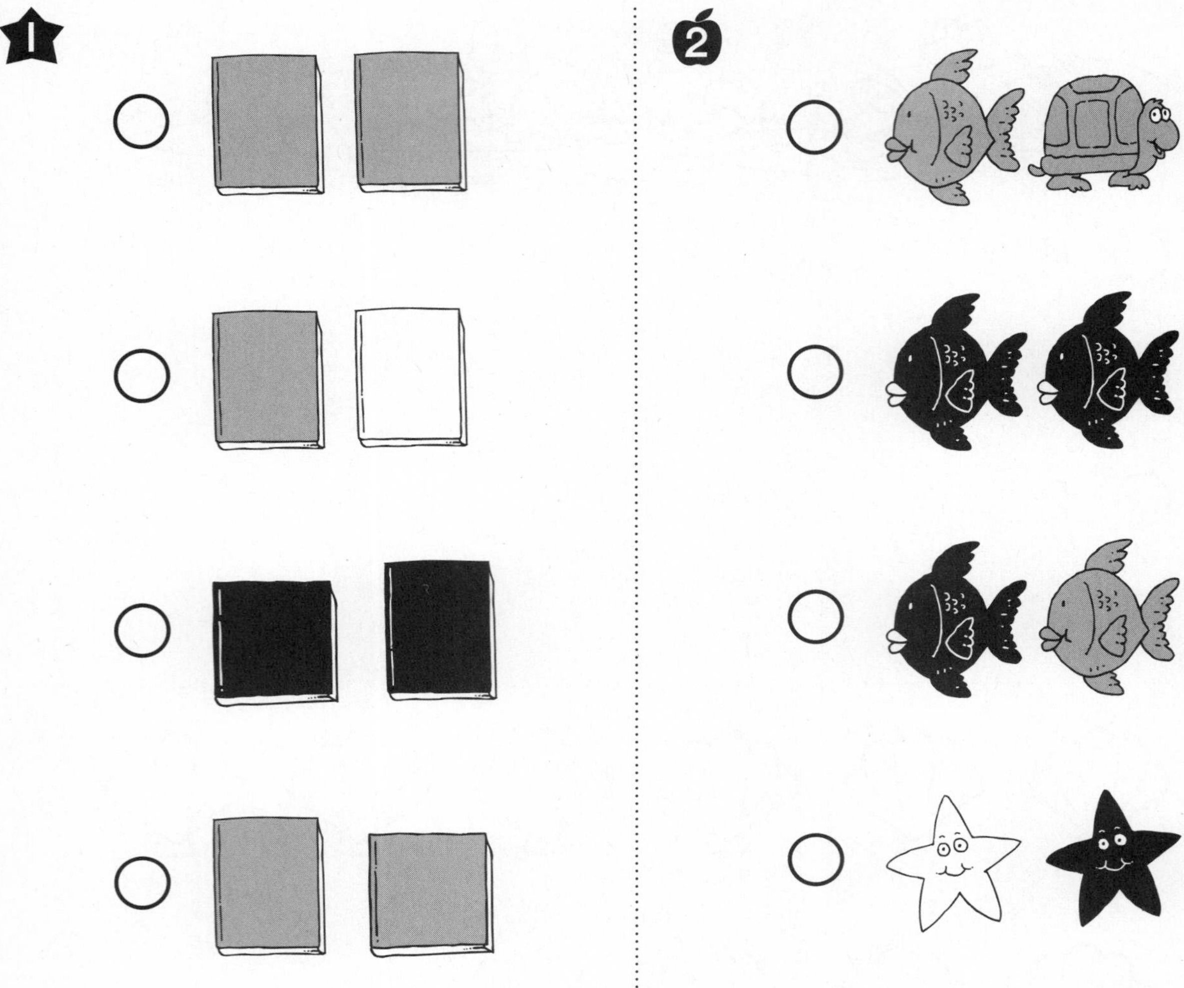

3

Directions Have students: 1 fill in the bubble next to the picture that shows objects that are the same shape and same color; 2 fill in the bubble next to the picture that shows objects that are the same color and same kind; 3 draw 2 balls that are different from each other.

Name ____________________

Daily TEKS Review
13-2

1

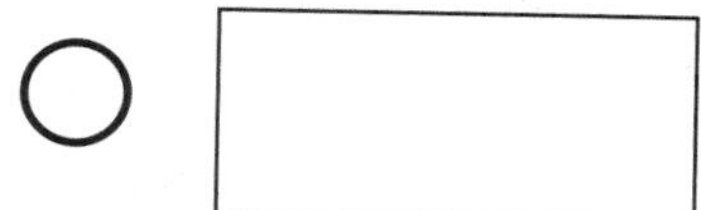

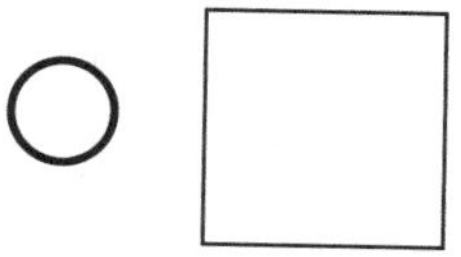

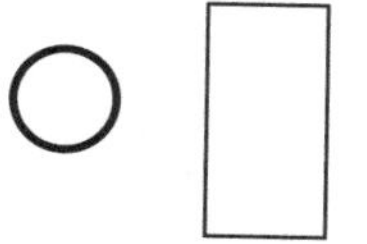

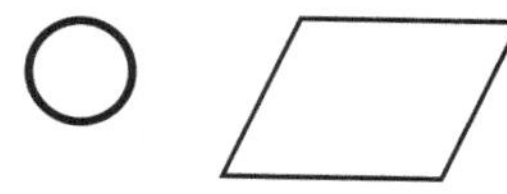

2

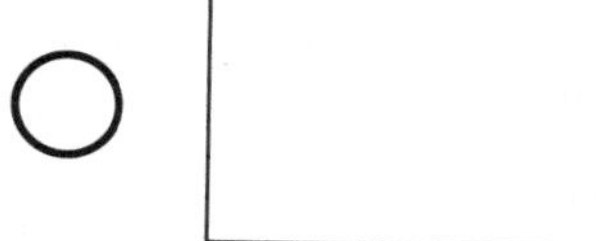

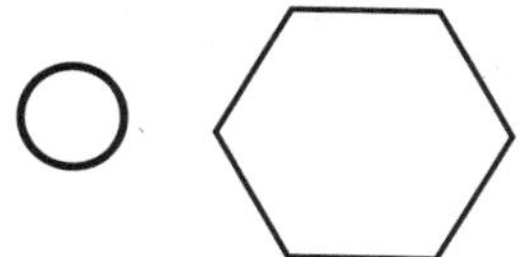

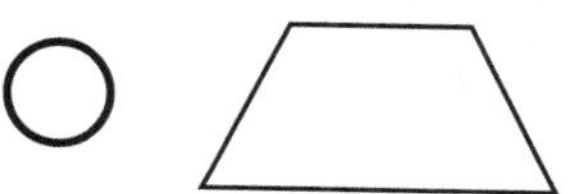

3

Directions Have students: 1 fill in the bubble next to the square; 2 fill in the bubble next to the rectangle; 3 count the seahorses, and then write the number that tells how many.

Name ________________________________

○ 10

○ 8

○ 7

○ 4

2

○ 

○ 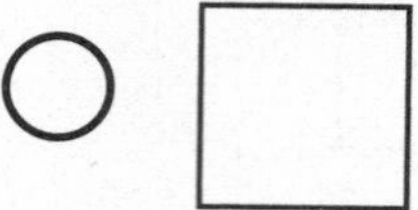

○ 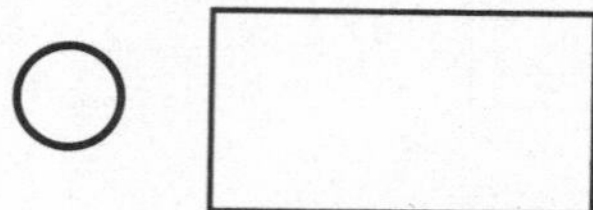

○ 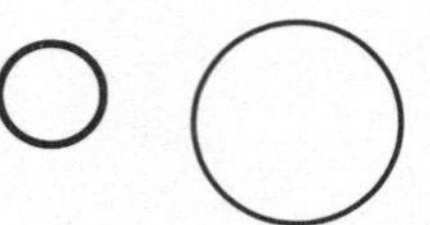

3

______

______

Directions Have students: 1 fill in the bubble next to the number that tells how many stars; 2 fill in the bubble next to the triangle; 3 count the puppies, and then write the number that tells how many.

Name ______________________

○ 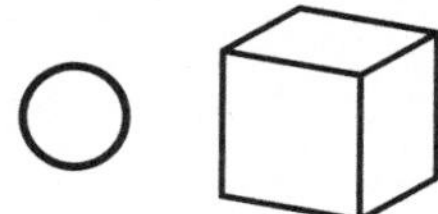

○ 

○ 

○ 

○ 10

○ 9

○ 8

○ 5

  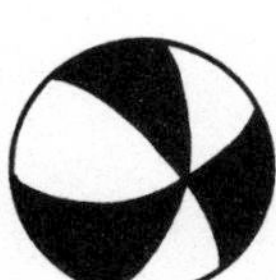    

______ − ______ = ______

Directions Have students: 1 fill in the bubble next to the sphere; 2 fill in the bubble next to the number that tells how many balloons; 3 write a subtraction sentence to match the picture.

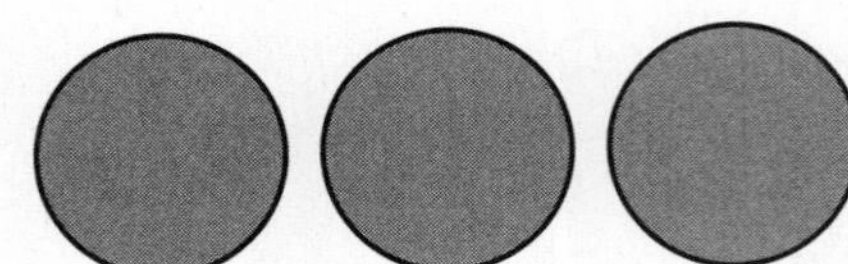

○ 

○ 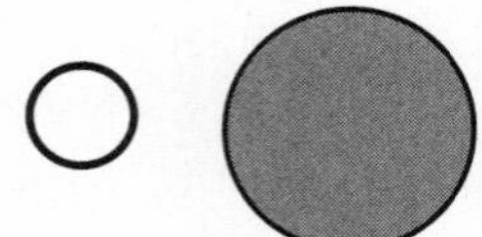

○ 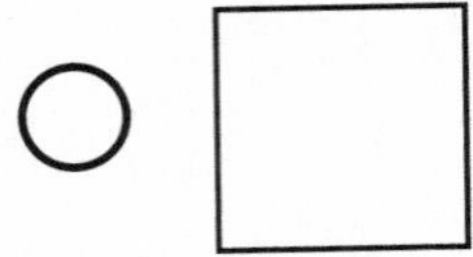

○ 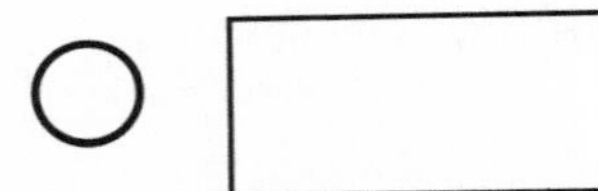

2 

○ 2

○ 3

○ 4

○ 5

3 4 + 1 = ______

______ − ______ = ______

Directions Have students: **1** fill in the bubble next to the shape that belongs in the group at the top; **2** fill in the bubble next to the number that is 2 more than 3; **3** finish the addition sentence, and then write a related subtraction sentence.

Name ______________________________

Daily TEKS Review
14-1

○ 2 + 0 = 2 ○ 2 + 2 = 4

○ 2 + 1 = 3 ○ 3 + 1 = 4

____

Directions Have students: 1 fill in the bubble next to the number sentence that tells how many; 2 count the pine cones, and then write the number that tells how many.

Name ______________________

Daily TEKS Review
14-2

4 5 6 ? 8

- ○ 9
- ○ 7
- ○ 6
- ○ 0

○ ○ ○ ⊗ ⊗

- ○ 5 − 2 = 3
- ○ 5 − 4 = 1
- ○ 5 − 3 = 2
- ○ 5 − 5 = 0

3

○ ○ ○   ○ ○ ○ ○

_____ + _____ = _____

_____ + _____ = _____

Directions Have students: 1 fill in the bubble next to the missing number; 2 fill in the bubble next to the subtraction sentence that matches the picture; 3 write 2 addition sentences that show joining the 2 groups of counters.

Name ______________________________

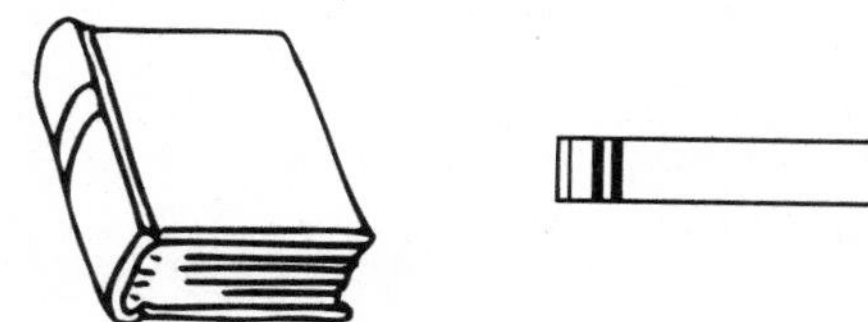

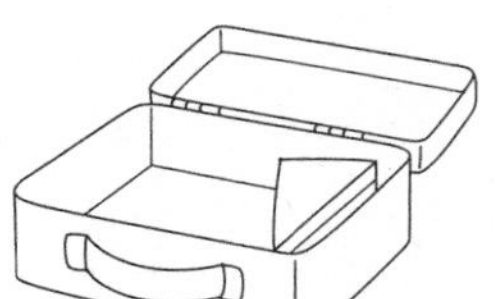

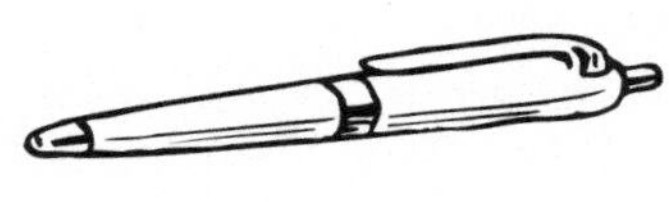

Directions Have students: 1 fill in the bubble next to the group that has more than 4 apples; 2 circle the objects that belong in the group of items that are used for writing.

Name ______________________

Daily TEKS Review
14-4

2

Directions Have students: 1 fill in the bubble next to the group that has more than 5 stars; 2 circle the writing tool that is longer than the marker at the top.

Name ______________________________

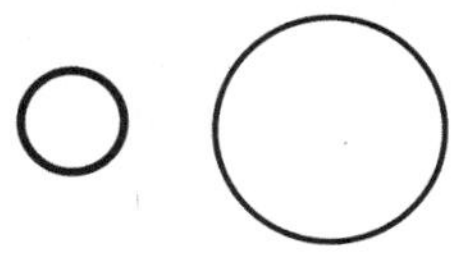

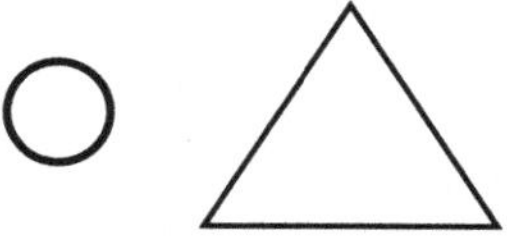

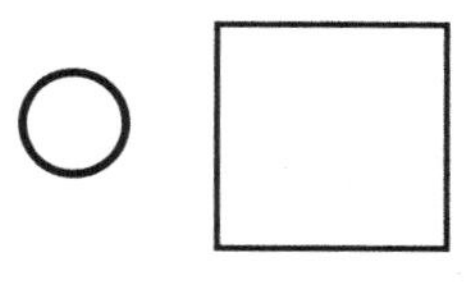

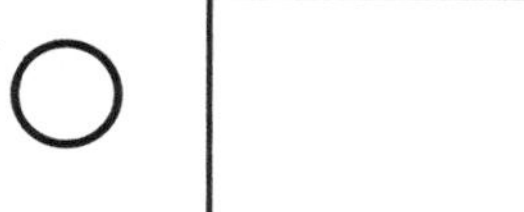

3

Directions Have students: 1 fill in the bubble next to the square; 2 color red the fish that are bigger and blue the fish that are smaller; 3 look at the fish bowl above, and then write an addition sentence that shows joining the 2 groups of fish.

Name ______________________________

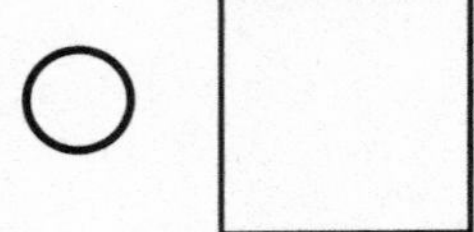

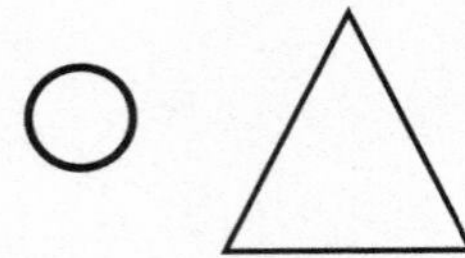

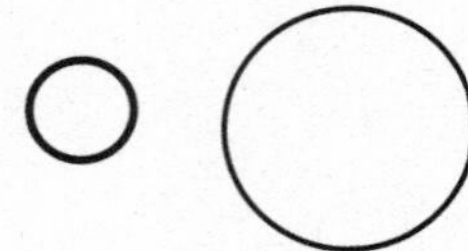

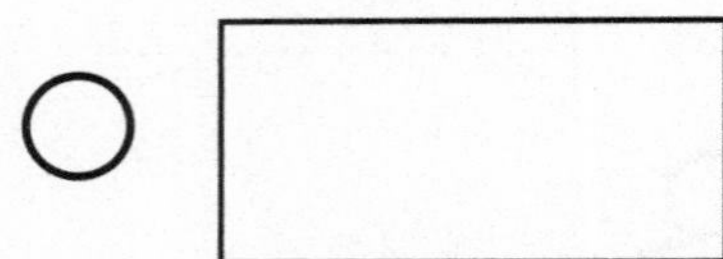

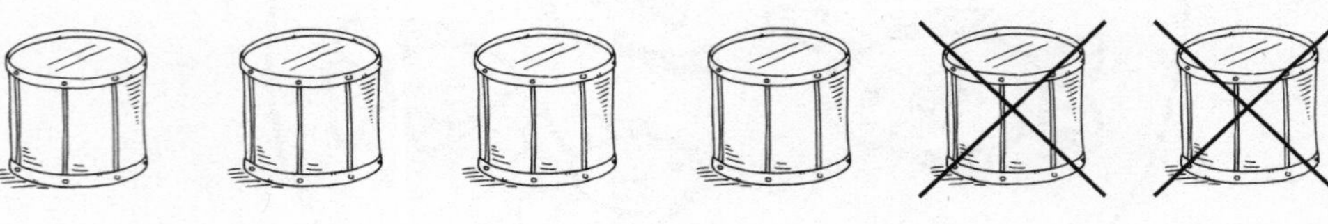

______ − ______ = ______

Directions Have students: 1 fill in the bubble next to the circle; 2 write a subtraction sentence that matches the picture.

Name ______________________________

Daily TEKS Review
15-1

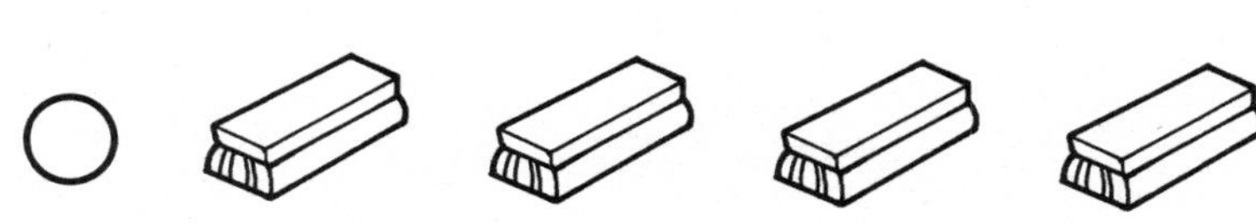

Directions Have students: 1 fill in the bubble next to the picture that shows 4 erasers; 2 look at the row of shapes at the top, and then draw a row with 1 more, a row with 1 fewer, and a row that shows the same number of shapes.

Name ______________________

1 34

- ○ 34
- ○ 32
- ○ 35
- ○ 33

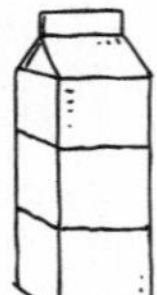

2

○ ○

○ ○

3 8 9 7

______ ______ ______

Directions Have students: 1 fill in the bubble next to the number that comes after 34 when counting forward by 1s; 2 fill in the bubble next to the picture that shows the container that holds the same as the one at the top; 3 write the numbers in order from least to greatest.

Name ________________________________

Daily TEKS Review
15-3

○    ○ 

○    ○ 

2

○ $2 + 3 = 5$ ○ $5 + 3 = 8$

○ $2 + 5 = 7$ ○ $4 + 4 = 8$

3

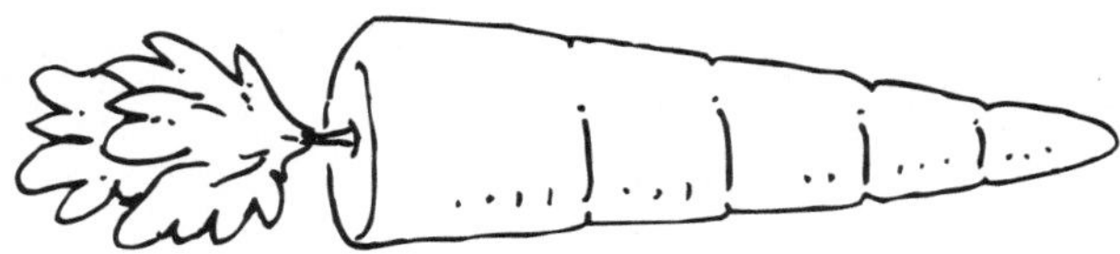

Directions Have students: 1 fill in the bubble next to the picture that shows an object that is lighter than a shoe; 2 fill in the bubble next to the addition sentence that shows joining the groups of pigs; 3 draw a longer carrot below the one shown.

Name ____________________

Daily TEKS Review
15-4

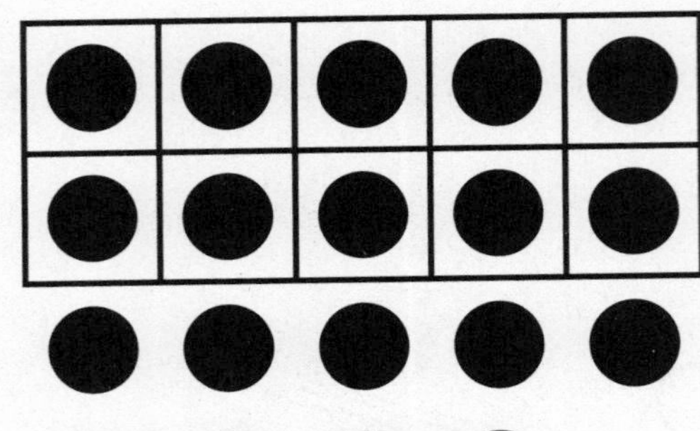

○ 16

○ 17

○ 18

○ 19

2

______ + ______ = ______

Directions Have students: 1 fill in the bubble next to the number that tells how many counters; 2 write an addition sentence that shows joining the groups of rabbits.

Name ______________________

Daily TEKS Review
15-5

2

 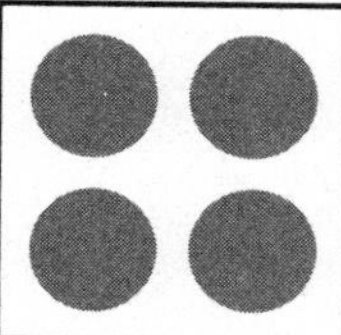

 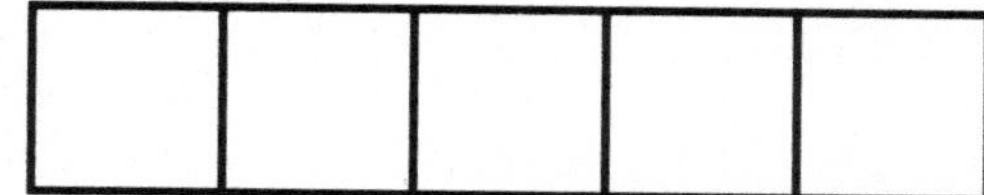

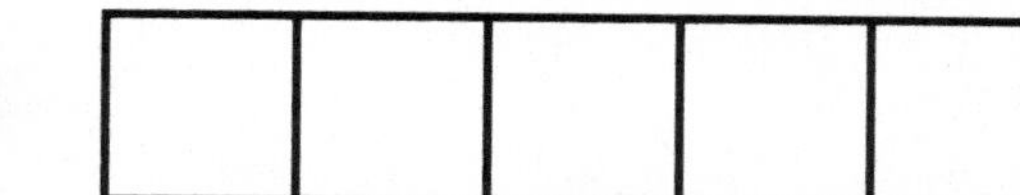

3

10, 20, 30, 40, ______

Directions Have students: 1 draw counters to show 2 fewer counters than bears; 2 color a box on the graph for each counter, and then circle the counter next to the row that has fewer; 3 write the number that comes next when you count by 10s.

Name ______________________

Daily TEKS Review
16-1

1 $4 + 5 =$ ______

- ○ 5
- ○ 9
- ○ 45
- ○ 54

2

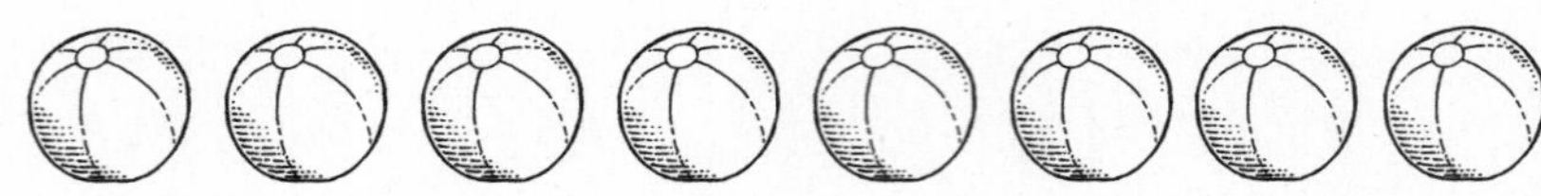

- ○
- ○
- ○
- ○

3

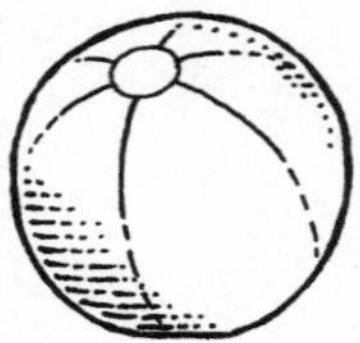

Directions Have students: **1** fill in the bubble next to the number that completes the addition sentence; **2** fill in the bubble next to the group that shows 2 fewer balls than the group at the top; **3** draw an object with the same shape as the ball.

Name ______________________

Daily TEKS Review
16-2

1

○ $10 = 7 + 3$

○ $10 = 6 + 4$

○ $10 = 2 + 8$

○ $6 = 4 + 2$

2

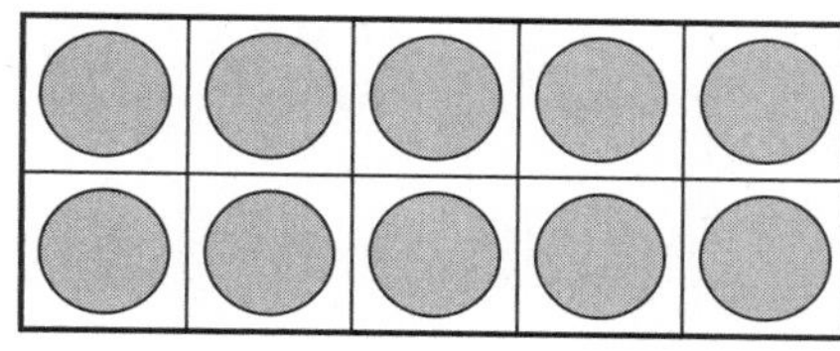

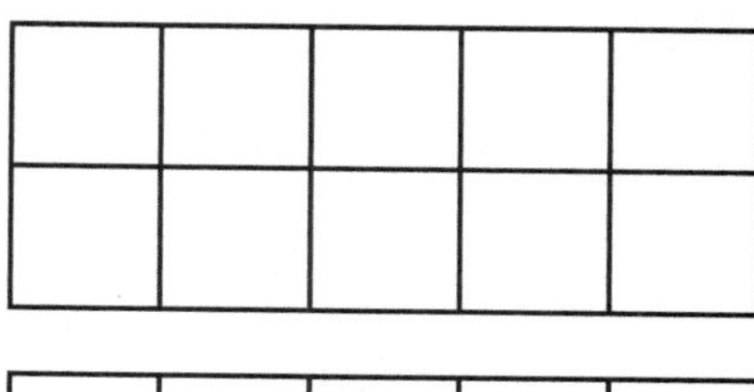

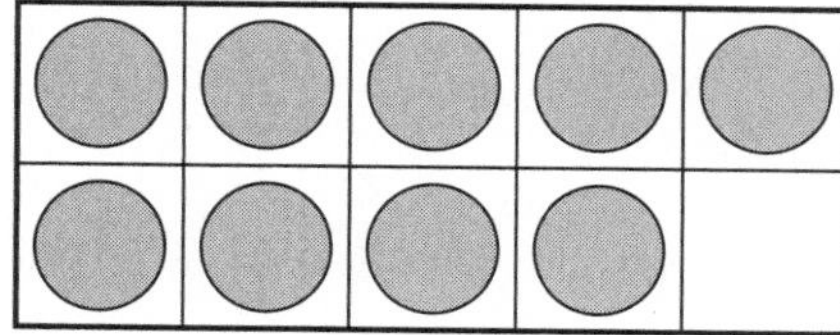

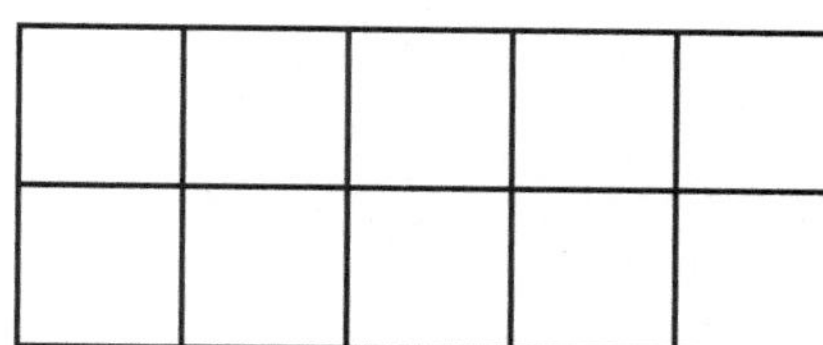

______

Directions Have students: **1** fill in the bubble next to the number sentence that shows joining the 2 groups of color tiles; **2** count the counters, write the number that tells how many, and then draw a set of counters on the right that has 2 more.

Name ______________________

○ 

○ 

○ 

○ 

2

Directions Have students: 1 fill in the bubble that shows 7 desks; 2 count the apples in the basket, and then write the number that tells how many.

Name ______________________________

Daily TEKS Review
16-4

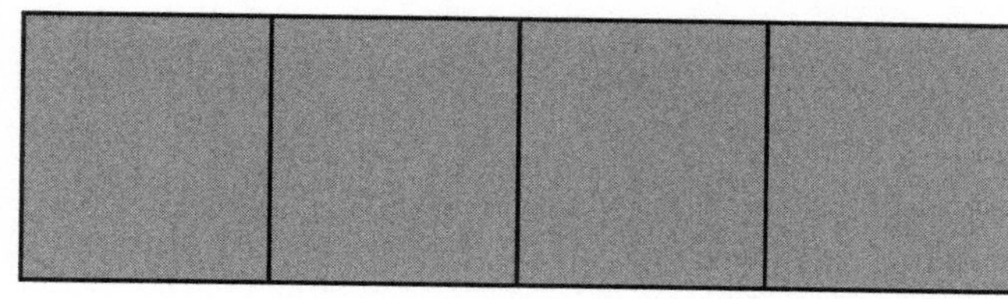

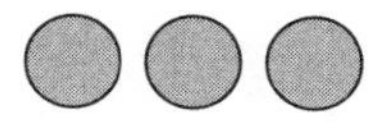

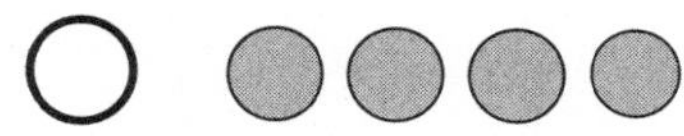

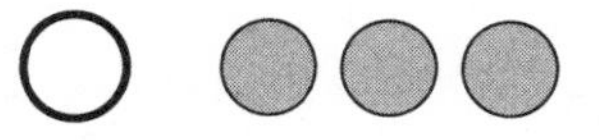

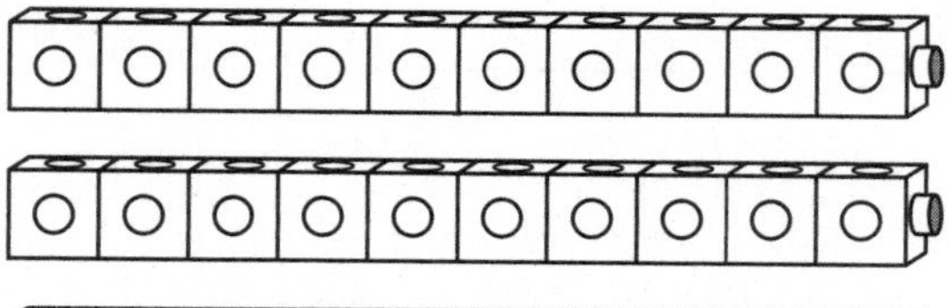

____

Directions Have students: 1 fill in the bubble next to the row that has the same number of creatures as colored boxes at the top; 2 fill in the bubble next to the row that shows 2 fewer counters than the row at the top; 3 count the cubes by 10s, and then write the number that tells how many.

Name ______________________

○ 💧💧💧💧💧

○ 💧💧💧💧💧💧

○ 💧💧💧💧💧💧💧

○ 💧💧💧💧💧💧💧💧

2 3, 4, __?__, 6

○ 7 ○ 2

○ 5 ○ 1

3

______ ◯ ______ = ______

Directions Have students: 1 fill in the bubble next to the row with 7 raindrops; 2 fill in the bubble next to the missing number; 3 write a number sentence that shows joining the groups of animals.